The authors would like to thank the following:

Esther Whitby, Eileen Evanson, Daly Maxwell, Stephen Young, Dennis Smyth, Jo Graham, Richard Hayden, Colette Fagan, Ivan Maginnis of the Housing Executive, Martin Turnbull, Robert Fraser, Ian Kirk-Smith, David Lavery, Dessie McCandless, Paul McNamee, Naimh O'Hagan, Islington Borough Council, The London Borough of Tower Hamlets, Christine Mountgomery, Michael Longley, Stanley McIlreevy, Mark and Liz Johnson, Robin and Una and, of course, Mary Ann.

CONTENTS

Sometimes he suspected that he loved them as God does – at a judicious distance.

CHRISTOPHER MORLEY

LONDON

ONE

The evening was a brown blur. Hackney hummed and twitched with light and noise like a sleeping dog. Kingsmead Estate was hell's breath on a Friday night. Hally and I sat on the bottom step of a communal staircase, drinking a brand of beer I've never liked. Without desire, we watched the teenage girls in belt-length skirts patrolling the estate. We listened to the jeer and chatter of the fightsome boys, chivvying and heckling the girls. We counted the lighted windows as they blinked out to darkness.

My companion was in a corrosive mood. Hally had ceased to be a father a couple of weeks previously. His two young daughters had been taken into care. He had been evicted from his Kingsmead flat a week later. His wife had left him six months before and he knew nothing of her whereabouts. In a few days' time, he was due to appear in court on a shop-lifting charge, his third offence of this kind. He was almost assured of a custodial sentence. When I met Hally, he was staying at a friend's place, sleeping on a sofa in the sitting room of a two-bedroomed flat with five other occupants.

Hally was hurt. He was a wounded, limping man. He had failed as a husband, as a father and as a householder. He had failed as a citizen. The rest of us, the confident majority, we were about to give Hally a very hard time. He was twenty-nine but he felt like my grandfather and looked older. His movements had the cumbersome fragility of the old and the defeated. He spoke without pleasure, convinced of the futility of his story.

He told me that, just before it had all finally fallen apart for him, his rent arrears had been close to £1800. He was still paying instalments on fuel bills of two years before and his electricity had been cut off for a month. His combination of arrears was such that his benefit payments had become theoretical, algebraic. The real money was almost all removed at source by the local authority or DSS to pay off outstanding debt. For months he had survived nine or ten days out of every fortnight with the sum of £5 or less in cash. Money astounded him. It had become something he could not imagine or fully comprehend. Money had defeated Hally. It had routed him utterly.

Hally was a nice man. Fit, once vigorous and still intelligent. I liked Hally. Facing what he faced – imprisonment, homelessness, solitude and despair – Hally oozed hurt. He suffered a rage of pain and loss. That night, he spoke longingly of hiding, of surrender. He talked of climbing into some bed and pulling the covers over his head until everything had gone away and everyone forgotten about him. As he spoke, he slumped further on to the steps where we sat. A car passed and its headlights waved a band of light across us. Hally's face was puffy and streaked with tears.

I got out of there. Muttering some specious platitudes and making plans for further meetings which neither of us believed, I hopped off and left him. As I walked away, I tried to summon some ginger thoughts of success, comfort or home. I looked at the sky, blunt and yellow over the badly lit estate. Arguments, pleading or irate, were loud all around. I felt pressed and reluctant, as if I were treading slack water.

Before I had left him, Hally told me how different money looked from his end.

'It's impossible. It becomes a joke. The more you get into debt and the less you bring in – the more money looks like a dream you had. Once I had to buy a pair of shoes for Sarah [his eight-year-old daughter]. I only needed a tenner. Ten fucking quid! For weeks I broke my heart trying to get that money together. I couldn't. Everything went on food for the kids or paying off the debts. Sarah cried every night because the kids at school laughed at her old shoes. I was so ashamed. I was supposed to be a father and I couldn't even get my hands on ten quid to buy my girl a pair of shoes. In the end, I *had* to nick them.'

Though money had just become an easy thing, falling into my lap from unexpected places, the change had been recent enough for me to remember when money had indeed seemed impossible. An enemy that punished, shamed and wounded you. Hally's problem was simple. It was all to do with money. Though a citizen of a capital city in Western Europe, Hally was forced to steal a pair of shoes for his child. It's hard for many of us to *imagine* that kind of relationship with money but it's easy to understand.

Stories like Hally's get you down. They embarrass or appal. They can really ruin your day. That's why I left so abruptly that night. That's why most of us exit hurriedly when we meet someone like Hally blearily weeping. We can't afford to listen to their dreams of analgesia and narcosis. It's the same for most of us, however sympathetic. Who can honestly bear too much exposure to tales of murderous poverty? Who truly needs or wants to know?

Poverty is a strange thing. It's timeless, international and seemingly permanent. It is tolerated, ignored and endured. It is a happy hunting ground for sociologists, economists and doctrinaire moralists. Some say it doesn't really exist. Some say it exists but that it is impossible to define. It's a product of self-inflicted industrial decline. It's an evolutionary safeguard. It's a consequence of capitalist conspiracy. It's the will of God.

There's an appetite for the prosperous babble of poverty talkers. We're interested. Newspapers run the story, television treats it and fiction distorts it (though not as much as governments). Books about poverty are written and read. You prove that as much as I.

It's surprising really. Poverty is an uncomfortable issue. I'm sure it causes most of us shame or annoyance. Thinking about poverty can disturb and disrupt privilege. It can ruin a good dinner and take some of the jolly glow from a generous bank balance. In London I've watched the wealthy watch the un-wealthy and I've seen their obvious discomfort and perplexity. I've seen their failure to cope with what they can decreasingly ignore.

So, considering the ticklish nature of our contemplation of the poor, it is truly remarkable that so much interest and concern at best (and prurience at worst) survives our natural bent for thoughtlessness. Why do we still risk such disruption to our ease and comfort? Why do we, if we are not poor, bother thinking about those that are poor at all?

I'd hazard a guess that we continue to be interested because many of us feel that poverty is not really that far away. If fragile parts of our lives that make us prosperous were removed, we would be bereft and helpless as any. If our jobs, houses, cars were taken away; if we were stripped of our privilege, property and assets, earned or inherited, we would be poor. Poverty is possibly the only human experience apart from birth or death that every human being is capable of sharing. We can't all be healthy, intelligent, wealthy or strong. Some people could never run a diary or work by telephone; others could scarcely make the tea on a building site. Numeracy or physical dexterity are not the lot of all. Few of us are born into privilege, we can't all handle money, machinery or farmland. But we can all be poor. And we can all fear it.

Long lists of human results owe their origin to poverty. Fewer people now acknowledge these. In the fiscal orgy of the last twelve years or so, poverty has been seen as a minor consequence of certain necessarily macho economic strategies. In all the crowding tough talk, money idolatry and media cel-ebration, poverty has almost ceased to be seen as a human predicament. It has become an idea, an anachronistic notion. It is not seen as something that distorts or destroys people's lives. Poverty has been annulled.

Poverty is *not* difficult to define. Poverty is a state of want or deprivation that gravely interferes with someone's life. Those who want to work but can't; those who want to feed their families adequately but can't; those who want to clothe themselves and their children decently but can't; those who want to live in habitable housing conditions but can't; those who want to educate themselves or their children but can't; those whose lives are made smaller by lack of money. These people are poor. They're poor. That's what they are.

Recently, poverty has become a contested notion. A war is being waged to establish ownership over its idea – to be entitled to define and set perimeters on poverty. In this struggle the poor are largely ignored or patronized. They are seldom treated as people with their own particularity and their own dignity. Unheard or voiced-over, it is they who have to endure deprivation and its multiple opprobrium.

I had already been working on this book for a couple of months when I met Hally. I was already running scared and wounded by the scale and complexity of some of the suffering I'd seen. He brought me faster to the end of my tether. Not long after meeting him, I was on a plane back home to Belfast, scared and running.

I don't know precisely what I was thinking about when I decided to write this book. I'm not sure why I chose to write about London, Glasgow and Belfast. I can barely remember what I hoped for, dreaded or expected. I recall that when Donovan and I first arrived in London, I was hugely pessimistic. Donovan, the demon genius photographer (his first book published when he was eighteen) was full of confidence. But he, too, felt, strangely stalled. We lingered over glutinous cups of coffee in a café at Heathrow. I felt fraudulent already. I was the last man qualified to write about the 'dispossessed'. I felt like a mountebank. I was a novelist. A paid liar. What was I doing here?

Later that day, Donovan and I stood on Waterloo Bridge and watched the river. He was excited about London, a city he barely knew, bellicose with precocity. He seemed sure that his talent, his pictures would be capable of presenting dispossession in all its bones and blood to the Home Counties Reluctants. It was getting late and we still had nowhere firm to sleep that night. I was growing anxious. Donovan smiled reassuringly at me.

'I suppose we had better find some poor people,' he said.

And, sadly, we found them with ease. There were more than plenty to go round. But they found us, too. There wasn't much of us to spare. What had I expected? That I could objectively notate and dissect a series of poverty's evils, its grand aggregate of cruelty and suffering? Donovan and I had set out looking for poverty, unpleasantness and loss. We found it. We'd been happy in the belief that this loss and suffering would be other people's misery. But what we saw and heard diminished us in ways we could not have expected. London was falling apart and people were drowning, racked and bedevilled by want. We shouldn't have expected that we could walk away from that.

TWO

Hackney is like a shelf filled with twentieth-century fiction. Tales of loss, abandonment and abnegation are everywhere you look. The titles on the spines of the streets promise absorption and despair. It hurts to hear what a lot of people in this area can tell you. Poverty, decay and dispossession has caused damage to these people. No one escapes these things. But there are vignettes of individuality, intelligence, decency and many other deeply human incalculables. People are marked by poverty but they have other attributes, other problems, other successes.

Hackney is a strip of different films. Some parts of Hackney are pretty, close to gentrified. Some parts make West Belfast look like Knightsbridge. When first in Hackney I knew that I was somewhere poor. Hackney's loss is visible, it's patent. In most depressed areas, the true poverty opera takes place in the tiny rooms of council flats and houses. You have to get inside to see how bad it is. It is conducted in privacy. When I was growing up in West Belfast, I thought that my family were the poorest people in the city. Hackney's different. It's fooling no one. The houses are marked by want more visibly than the people. Some crumble on to paths, others collapse inwards, a last gesture of shame. Blocks are stained with filth or paint, pock-marked by glassless windows. Maintenance and repair are a nostalgic dream in Hackney.

That people were prepared to talk to me in so much detail must be an indication of how public is their ordeal. Would *you* tell me about your financial embarrassments? The sanitation history of your home? I certainly wouldn't. People told me of events of consequence and privacy in their lives. They told me of impossible, shameful things. Feats of self-maintenance with sums of money that embarrassed or enraged me. A family of five who due to a benefit delay had survived for a fortnight on £15. A young man who had eaten only once every two days for more than a month after losing his job (redundancy payments are a dream here). A pensioner couple who had not eaten a cooked meal in six months. In the face of such testimony, outrage is facile. God, this is bad, you think. This is just terrible. It shouldn't happen. People shouldn't have to cope with hardship as unnecessary and vicious as this. People shouldn't have to *tell* you about this.

Henry Richards was a twenty-two-year-old West Indian from the Nightingale Estate. He was unemployed but permanently hopeful of a job. 'I've got six GCEs. One day somebody isn't going to ignore that.' I hadn't known him long and was wary of saying what I did. I suggested that it might also have to include ignoring his colour. Henry was surprised by this. (He told me much later on that he'd figured me as a classic white liberal – someone who would pretend he wasn't black.) He thought about it for a moment. Then he asked me whether I would give him a job if I was an employer. I replied that his colour would make no difference. 'There you are,' he said, 'you can't be the only one who thinks like that?'

Henry took me to a local street market where he sometimes worked on one of the stalls. With this haphazard (and illegal) addition to his fortnightly dole cheques, his average income averaged out about £40–45 per week. Compared with many other young men whom I had met this was absurdly prosperous. Later, I discovered that he gave his mother £20 per week to help out at home. He was popular in this market and even helped me get one or two bargains. He invited me back to his home for dinner. I was flattered and surprised. I accepted.

On our way back to the Nightingale Estate, Henry and I talked about literature. I hate to show myself as an ignorant snob but I was surprised at the scope and extent of Henry's reading. Jane Austen bored him. He liked Dickens (he'd read *Great Expectations* and *Hard Times*, appropriately enough). He made unprintable remarks about Thomas Hardy. The weird characteristic of Henry's unexpected erudition was that it featured almost exclusively nineteenth-century novelists. He explained that this was because most of the books that he could afford to buy were secondhand school texts, the bulk of which appeared to be nineteenth-century fiction. The idea of economic necessity forming an entire taste in literature was both grotesque and inspiring. Henry was a reader any writer would have been proud to have.

The dinner that Henry's mother cooked was exotic and delicious. Here we go again, I thought. Where's the single slice of white bread among fifteen people? I watched the way Henry operated at home. The tenderness and open affection with which he jibed at the women of his family (mother and three sisters) was unaffected and appealing. The burden of sole male lay very lightly on his elegant shoulders. I found myself increasingly drawn to Henry. Handsome, charismatic, bright and amiable, he was the total school hero. He was the boy other boys liked. Don't get me wrong, Henry would have been nice if he'd been earning fifteen grand a year. Poverty doesn't make any one personality or characteristic particularly noble, but when Henry's mother told me how he had more or less taken over the family when her husband had left, Henry's *élan* and high spirits seemed pretty good going. Henry had been thirteen when his father had disappeared. He immediately started work in the markets after school and did a paper round before school. This information put his academic achievements into a new perspective. Few people could have remained literate, never mind manage to pass examinations, under such circumstances.

After dinner, the two girls left and Henry's mother chased us out of the flat good-naturedly. She had some friends coming round. I suggested to Henry that we might go to a bar but he demurred. We bought some bottles of beer and ended up on the green of Hackney Downs. We sat there for three hours, drinking and talking. Henry had a lot to say.

'The humiliations you get when you're signing on or when you've got a claim going are routine. Everybody knows about them. Even people who've never been on the dole in their life know it's a terrible thing to have to do. You're always seeing dole offices on TV – the queues, the dirt, the shame and all that. What people don't see is the crap you get if you're naïve enough to keep on looking for work. Careers officers and Job Centres trying to sell you bullshit jobs that are going to pay you less than £60 a week. Or interviews. Nobody sees what they can do to you at interviews. I've been to some job interviews which have been incredible. Like with being black, it's got to the stage where nobody openly says, like fuck off, nigger, but you know it's there all the time.'

Henry hotted up as he spoke. His hands chopped the air in rapid movements, impatient rather than angry.

'I don't have a criminal record. I've never committed a crime in my life. And yet at almost every interview I've been to they've hassled me about a criminal record. I've already said on the application form that I don't have a criminal record but it's like they don't believe me. They keep on about it. "Are you absolutely sure you don't have one? It's an offence to withhold information." I mean these fuckers are calling me a liar for no reason. Do you honestly think that they'd give a white guy that kind of grief? It pisses you off, that does.'

Despite this history and his present straitened circumstances, Henry remained optimistic about his chances of decent employment.

'I've had a couple of good jobs. Once I was working in a shop in Fulham. A real yuppie dive. I was getting £115 a week. Doesn't sound much maybe but it was fucking unbelievable to us. The shop was part of a chain and the area manager used to come round quite a bit to check up on what was going on in each branch. I used to have this kind of patter going with the customers – all these white yuppies. They loved it. Like they

could actually have a laugh with a black man, like I was a buddy
or something. Our area manager saw this a couple of times and
told me I was doing a great job. He started talking about a pay
rise and I said something about the idea of commission maybe
being better for both of us. He loved that. It was cheeky. He
thought I was fucking Henry Ford or Rockefeller or somebody
like that. He asked me if I'd thought about managing a shop.
Apparently there was going to be this vacancy in Ealing.

'The assistant manager of our shop saw this and he really
hated it. He was a real fat, stupid bastard. He started making
life difficult for me. Whenever the shop manager wasn't there,
this guy would go right over the top. I'd have to sweep up the
shop. Wipe the shelves and all that kind of shit. Anyway, this
guy ended up by trying to dock my pay for bad time-keeping.
I'd been there nine months and I'd only been late three times.
The latest was half an hour and that was with getting the buses
across to Fulham. I said this to the manager but she showed me
that this assistant manager had marked me down as late about
twenty times. I tried to point out to the manager that it was a
bit funny that I was only marked late when she was on the late
shift – like, on his word. She didn't care and I was gone. Two
weeks' pay and no chance of an industrial tribunal or anything
like that because I'd only been there for nine months. Then six
weeks with no dole. It wasn't funny.'

I'd already heard many such tales of victimization. Some of
them undoubtedly varied in truthfulness. I actually tried to
check this one out with the (well-known) company that Henry
had worked for. This investigation didn't get far but from the
obstruction I got at company headquarters and the panic when
I called the Fulham shop, it seemed probable that there must
have been some truth in what Henry had told me. Henry told
me that when he was leaving, the assistant manager had started
abusing him, revealing an encyclopaedic grasp of racial abuse.
Henry's reaction to this summed up the sagacious fatalism
among the poorly paid when it came to consequence and retribution.

'I could have hit this guy. He was a fat, ugly bastard. I could have really given it to him. Nobody calls me a black bastard without knowing I'm gonna want to clock him one – that's what this guy was trying to do to me. He wasn't satisfied with me losing my job. He wanted me in bigger trouble. He was going out of his way to get me into bother. Jesus, he was even prepared to get beaten up to get me into trouble. He must have really hated black people to do that. When you come up against hate like that . . . what can you do? There's no answer to hate like that.'

Henry's experiences had little to do with Henry the man. His friends had all suffered similar indignities. Their particular brand of poverty was altered and increased by the colour of their skin. They were black and that was enough. Enough to do them serious harm. Though many people claim that being black isn't necessarily an extra handicap for the black poor, I can't imagine that anyone, deep in themselves, seriously believes that. It's simple. A higher proportion of the black or coloured community in Britain is unemployed. The difference in percentage between black and white joblessness changes from year to year but it's always to the disadvantage of black people. Nobody really disputes this.

Liberal England still struggles with colour (illiberal England doesn't struggle at all). The politically correct Caucasian *copes* with black people by trying to pretend that they are not black. It's frivolous to think that being black doesn't make any difference. It does.

Henry's colour, his blackness, affected everything that happened to him. His employment history had been irrevocably marked and marred by it. His constant harassment by the police (I saw some of it) was a by-product of his blackness. His blackness attracted malice and futility from all sides. Degrading and absurd things happened to Henry because he was black. I'd met black people before. I was used to their stories of abuse and disenfranchisement. They were shocking stories. But these people had been educated, confident people. Henry and his friends were black and poor. They were robbed of two kinds of status, they suffered two sets of degradations.

None the less, Henry's stories were told with amusement rather than indignation. None of it seemed to light his fire unduly. His forbearance amazed me. I am Irish and spend my own days with radar searching for any incautious anti-Paddy murmurings. If I'd been Henry, I'd have been climbing the walls with fury. I asked him how he managed such equanimity. He peered at me cautiously before replying: he told me that he was gay as well.

'You try getting blue-arsed and agitated about being black or poor when you're gay as well. You don't get more marginal, you don't get more "dispossessed' than being a queer black man.'

I never saw Henry again. I liked Henry. He was absurdly blessed by life. Handsome, clever, buoyant, but deprived, black and gay. Henry was a cocktail of things it's hard to be. He seemed to handle it with great ease. Henry exemplified a strange and repulsive phenomenon – people who were as poor when they were employed as when they were jobless. Henry himself said that most of the time he couldn't tell the difference between the two states.

Many of the most cruelly deprived people I met were people in full- or part-time work. The plight of the low paid is nothing new but that doesn't make it all right. There seem to be an increasing number of employers who pay their workers repellently low wages. The catering industry in this country continues to be a disgrace. I encountered many people who worked fifty-hour weeks and were paid as little as £70 or £80 for their time. Construction tends to be well paid, sometimes almost absurdly so. Nevertheless, on sites where there are a great number of sub-contractors, legal or otherwise, basic labouring wages can fall to less than £100 with poor safety standards, fictional bonuses and no overtime. The cleaning industry is an area of deprivation often ignored since its employees are largely women. Wages in this profession can be absolutely astonishing. I met two middle-aged women from Bethnal Green, sisters, who cleaned offices for a well-known firm in the City of London. They worked twenty-eight hours a week for a take-home salary of £38.

Shirley from Martello Street in London Fields worked in a local dry-cleaners. She worked a week of never less than fifty hours and often more than sixty. She earned £78 per week. With the best of her overtime payments, her weekly wage had never climbed above £105. Shirley was married. Her husband was unemployed, he had been invalided out of his last job as a school caretaker. They lived with their three children, all of whom were over sixteen. I made a rough calculation of Shirley's benefit entitlements if she did not work. I found that they came to a sum of at least £50 more than she was paid for full-time work. This wasn't news to Shirley. I asked her why she continued working in such laborious conditions when she would be so much better off unemployed.

'I couldn't be happy without a job. God knows, me and my husband have been on the dole enough times for us to know what it's like and I just can't abide it. We make do well enough . . . I mean, there's never enough money but John gets his sick money and we always improvise. You can get round having no money if you're used to it. We've never really had money but we're not as bad off as some. There's a lot of people around London Fields with nothing, nothing at all. When I look at some of the people who live near us, I'm thankful for the little we've got.'

Sandy Wilson, a thirty-year-old Glaswegian father of two, worked on a large building site near Euston station. He worked forty-five hours a week for £120. The working conditions he described were appalling. The work was temporary, hugely sub-contracted. Sandy's job would dry up in two or three months. Safety precautions were non-existent. Sandy had never even been offered a hard hat. He didn't complain about this: anyone 'making trouble' was instantly dismissed. Casual labourers were often required to work whole days with only one break – a half-hour interruption for lunch. A sick day led to a day's wages being docked and if you stayed away for another day, you didn't need to bother going back. You would have been dismissed in your absence.

Sandy had worked on a great number of building sites around London. He didn't consider his present working conditions particularly bad. He had seen much worse. According to Sandy, the foremen were the worst part and the Clerk of Works on every site in the City was a qualified, certified bastard. A lot of labourers lost their jobs because they couldn't take the abuse that these men habitually meted out. Sandy was unmoved by it. Water off a duck's back, he said.

The point is not whether Shirley *can* 'get round' having so little money or whether Sandy *can* endure the insolence and abuse of his foremen, the point is whether they should have to suffer such things. The humiliations that the low paid suffer are extreme versions of universal complaints. Most employees suffer the pettiness and spite of their immediate superiors, many consider themselves underpaid. But for the low paid, for part-time workers, for homeworkers and casual workers, these problems are insoluble. There is no redress, no appeal against bad pay or conditions. Victimization and exploitation merely add themselves to the cocktail of stresses that the poorly paid worker already endures.

Many of the low paid are committing a criminal offence in working at all. Some claim benefit while working, others do not declare their income to the Inland Revenue and few pay National Insurance. These crimes are generally committed through necessity rather than cupidity. I met uncountable numbers of people whose benefit was completely inadequate for their needs, families who would have had to sacrifice clothing, heating, electricity or even a proper diet to stay on the right side of the law. These people considered the options and promptly broke the law. It seemed the prudent course for most. They had *no* alternative. Donovan remarked on the prevalence of people 'doing the double' among those he had photographed. He said that sometimes he felt as though he was taking mug-shots for police files. A kind of blameless rogues' gallery. It was odd, certainly. Everyone I met seemed to be breaking the law. They had to.

These people were illegally employed in two senses. Those for whom they worked were also committing a crime: they often did not declare their workers. They took refuge in a black-market workforce rendered safe by its size. Only the tiniest fraction of the casual workers that I encountered were 'officially' employed. The illegality does not stop there. Even if employers do put their entire workforce through the books, illegal working practices are widespread. Safety regulations, minimum wages, etc. are insolently flouted. For the low paid, for the black market of workers, decent working conditions, *legal* working conditions, are dependent on the benevolence of the employer. Altruism is rare.

The humiliations that the low paid endure are, to some degree, universal ones. Many of the stresses which they suffer are simply more intense versions of those stresses endured by the adequately paid as well. The harassment of management and immediate superiors, poor working conditions, inadequate safety standards, long hours and lack of job satisfaction. Dismissal, however, is a very different phenomenon for the poorly paid worker.

If the low-paid worker rejects his or her conditions, if he or she complains – they are almost always sacked. They rarely have any formal contract or union membership nor any recourse to industrial tribunals. They must turn again to the dole. If their work has been casual, they cannot inform the DSS of their dismissal. Even if their work has been legal, tax-paying employment, the DSS generally considers them to have made themselves voluntarily redundant. Their benefit is not paid for six weeks (in practice sometimes much longer). Recent DSS rule changes have made the plight of the suddenly redundant very unpleasant indeed.

At various times in my own life I have worked in a series of traditionally low-paid industries: construction, catering and retailing. The best paid by a very long way was the construction industry. I often laboured on London building sites. It was easy to find such work. There were unofficial pick-up sites for casual day work. A motley group of men would gather at a certain place in the City and vans would come by and select the young-est and fittest of the available crowd. I had many attractive advantages in finding such work. In common with a dispro-portionately large number of London building workers, I was Irish. I was young and healthy. I was flexible with certain statutory employment legalities. But most of all, and this is often ignored, I was male.

The work was arduous and, as Sandy Wilson claimed, often dangerous. The pay, however, was generally decent. The hours were reasonable, mostly restricted to the daylight hours (though I knew of several harsh round-the-clock sites in the West End). There was, in addition, a certain macho dignity about the work itself. It is proud work. A stable working-class occupation.

My time in the catering industry was very different. At one point I worked for a London agency which found its workforce temporary posts and charged the employer an hourly rate. That sum was divided almost equally between the agency and the worker. Despite this parasitic arrangement, these jobs weren't so bad. Dismissal was common since it was an easy matter to cancel a worker's booking and ask the agency for a replacement. On the other hand, it was also possible for the workers to refuse jobs that they found intolerable. There was plenty of work.

Such ease of dismissal led to many abuses. Almost anyone could cancel an agency temp's booking. Management scarcely needed to be involved. I was once dismissed from a very famous

London hotel by a cook because I objected to being called a 'Paddy bastard'. The drawbacks were obvious. Women were much more popular temps than men. Sexual harassment was the norm. Young black men were rejected or dismissed on the thinnest of pretexts. In another London hotel where I worked as a breakfast waiter, I witnessed daily racial harassment of the black members of the breakfast team by the deputy buttery manager. It took a lot of effort on his part since he and I were the only whites in a workforce of sixteen. In the month that I was there, eight people lost their jobs, only two of them voluntarily.

The pay for agency staff was slightly more than for permanent catering staff. The permanent staff felt this to be unjust since management did not have to pay an agency levy on their wages. In the summer of 1984 I averaged around £2 an hour which wasn't dreadful then. (It might have been dreadful if I had been anything other than a vacation-working student.) The biggest handicap for agency staff was the widespread practice of having their tips confiscated. One always secreted one's tips as much as possible. In one hotel I was forced to keep my tips in my underwear since I was actually frisked at the end of shifts to make sure I hadn't kept any.

My experience of working in shops and department stores was another catalogue of abuse and exploitation. Shop work, however, does not seem to be a common employment for the very poor. Shop assistants, generally, must present a standard of appearance expensive to maintain. Bizarrely the educational requirements for a successful application can also be fairly stringent. Thus the poor are mostly squeezed out of that humble industry.

Perhaps my most extreme experience of low-paid work was when I worked briefly as a security guard for a well-known company which serviced many of London's merchant banks. After a gruelling one-day training session, I was let loose on an unsuspecting society of wrong-doers. The hours were incredible – a minimum of between sixty-five and seventy hours per week.

The take-home pay for such hours was between £90–£115 per week. After a few weeks I began to witness a demonstration of the peculiar brand of higher mathematics that bedevils the low paid. I was working ever-increasing hours and yet found, to my real bewilderment, that my actual pay was *decreasing*. I checked my pay slips. I couldn't work it out. I'm not innumerate but the esoteric calculations involved defeated me. I approached the company, hoping that this disappearing income might be some weird mistake. I was sacked immediately, ostensibly for some non-existent time-keeping fault. I'm still owed a week's outstanding pay by that company.

Homeworkers, casuals and part-time workers suffer the worst conditions of the low paid. The poverty endured by the low-paid employed is similar in many ways to that endured by the unemployed and the dependant. Some might consider that the employed poor have the advantage of their time being occupied but in industries as depressing and joyless as those in which the low paid work, the opportunity for job-satisfaction is negligible.

I loathe the phrase 'vicious circle'. It's overused and frequently misapplied. Nevertheless, the plight of the low paid fully merits that tag. Large-scale unemployment and deprivation in economically weak regions make such employment practices possible and then increase their prevalence. Poor areas create communities desperate enough to tolerate such conditions. Employers leap on the opportunity of a workforce with such low expectations. Their exploitation becomes profitable. The low-paying businesses thus expand their operations, undercutting other businesses which may pay more. The expectations of the workforce are depressed further. Back to the beginning and round again. It is a horrible phenomenon.

Hackney is one of those parts of London saturated with businesses paying people Victorian wages for Victorian hours. Two pounds fifty and a packet of crisps per annum. An area can't survive like this. It can't maintain itself and grow when it shoots itself in the foot every day. No benefit accrues to a region where this is the primary type of commerce. Expressions like 'private enterprise', 'free trade' and 'capital growth' bring the house down in Hackney. Hackney laughs like a drain at these bright shadows. Any money made in Hackney isn't made *by* Hackney. Hackney's like a luckless schoolboy. The one who's last to be picked for the football team, the one whose lunch is stolen, the one with the patch on his spectacles, the boy who knows it isn't fair but isn't sure why.

THREE

Gabrielle told me that at one bad point she had maintained herself for three days on cups of tea with no milk and sugar and two bowls of boiled, salted rice each day. She said that she had felt nauseous, hungry, depressed and ashamed but added that for a couple of days at least her dreams had been unforgettable. Hunger had amazed her with its complexity and surprise. She would never dream such dreams again.

Gabrielle lived in the Kingsmead Estate in Hackney. On a long walk from Islington, you take a series of steps away from prosperity and its normality. There are a lot of grim places along that way: Dalston, Stonebridge Estate, Nightingale Estate. The end of that journey is Trowbridge Estate and Kingsmead. You'll struggle to find a more depressed, worked over part of London. For all the hushed talk of Catford, Thamesmead etc., for those who live in Kingsmead, Kingsmead is as bad as it gets.

Gabrielle was twenty-four years old. She had two children – Jack aged three and Mary aged five. Gabrielle was dauntingly clever and attractive. The children shared these gifts. On our first meeting I snooped around her sitting room while she made some coffee. The room was clean and comfortable. The sofa on which I perched seemed luxurious compared with some of the gear upon which I had parked my arse recently. The walls were occasionally punctuated with neatly framed posters heralding various London exhibitions. The television set was discreet in an obscure corner and the carpet was worn but presentable. There were arm-chairs, lamps, a clutch of ornaments on the electric fire. There was a bookshelf. There were books. I began to grow disheartened. I was seeking sensation. I wanted to find some *horribly* poor people. I needed urchins, tin baths, ancient cripples coughing their lungs on to their ragged sleeves. I was looking for a pantomime. I didn't want this woman. She had too much furniture and too much taste.

Gabrielle and I talked warily over our coffee cups. Jack, the three-year-old, dawdled around the flat, occasionally squatting among the rubble of his toys and creating desultory traffic situations with his model cars. He shared many of his mother's features but while she looked drawn and anxious, he was plump and robust; more than well fed. At one point, I was coerced into a complex two-hander involving an AA van, a broken down Volvo and a taxi cab. He was confident and alert when I played with him. He looked better buttered than the pampered children of my most middle-class friends.

Gabrielle and the children had been living in this flat for three months. Her husband, Tony, had walked out on her about a month before she moved to Kingsmead. They had been living in a rented flat somewhere off the Seven Sisters Road which Gabrielle had loved very much. Tony closed down their joint bank account, removed all of his belongings and quite a lot of hers and simply disappeared. Gabrielle was left with hardly any cash and only three weeks' grace before the rent was due. Tony, a well-paid mechanic, returned to the flat twice. On both occasions, Gabrielle asked him for money so that she could buy food for Jack and Mary. The first time, Tony refused. He and a friend removed some furniture and Tony beat up Gabrielle while his friend waited in the van. Five-year-old Mary called the police but they didn't show up.

The second time Tony came back, he seemed close to amiable. Gabrielle asked for money again. Tony didn't want to argue in front of the children. When they had left the room to discuss this privately, Tony forced her upstairs and raped her. Afterwards, he went downstairs and played with the children.

When he left, Gabrielle found a ten-pound note on the television set.

Gabrielle now began to search for somewhere to live. For some impenetrable reason (as so many of their reasons seem to be) the DSS told her that she would not be entitled to enough Housing Benefit to pay the rent of the Seven Sisters Road flat. Gabrielle was not sorry to leave it. She did not wish to remain where her husband could find her and continue his abuse. When the family had moved into the flat they had paid a month's rent in advance as well as a deposit against damage of £100. If Gabrielle could find somewhere else to live within three weeks she would realize a sum close to £400.

In those three weeks Gabrielle had fed and maintained herself and her children with the total sum of £52.53. On the day that Tony left she found £17.53 in her handbag (she was, unsurprisingly, very precise). She borrowed £15 from her mother, who lives on a state pension. Tony had, as we've seen, left her with the £10 compensation for raping her and she borrowed a further £10 from a close and sympathetic female friend. That Gabrielle successfully fed three people with such a sum is an astonishing achievement. That she actually moved house at the same time is scarcely credible.

The flat in which Gabrielle now lived was an illegal sub-let from the council's actual tenant – the friend who had lent Gabrielle the tenner. This munificent friend had moved in with her fiancé in another part of Kingsmead. Gabrielle paid her £15 per week. She could not claim Housing Benefit to cover this expense since the flat was illegally sub-let council property. The rent had to come out of the total weekly income (Family Income Support and Child Benefit) of £58 per week. After the inroads made by rent, food bills and other pathetic deficits from this fragile total, Gabrielle was left with her single weekly luxury, a single packet of cheap cigarettes. The cost of these fags was such an inordinate amount of her available weekly cash that Gabrielle was tormented by guilt about her three cigarettes a day.

She succeeded in moving the family to Kingsmead before the next month's rent was due on the Seven Sisters flat. She claims that she vacated the flat in good time and left it in very good condition, even repainting the room in which the children had slept. Despite this, the property agency refused to repay her the month's advance rent and the damage deposit to which she was entitled. After several acrimonious visits, Gabrielle took the children with her to the agency office. She loudly demanded the money that was rightfully hers and complained that her children were going hungry because of this non-payment. Apparently, some flat-hunting couples left when the row started and one or two people took her side, complaining to the staff about the way she was being treated. The manager saw the harm that was being done to his business and reluctantly agreed to give Gabrielle some money.

They gave her £150 instead of the £440 which was her right. In what seems to have been a purely malicious gesture, they refused to give her this sum in cash though they admitted that they had more than enough petty cash available. She would have to accept a cheque. Gabrielle protested that she no longer had a bank account but the agency persisted. She was too desperate and defeated to argue further. She accepted the cheque. It was a Friday afternoon. No bank would be open until Monday. Gabrielle had the bus fare back to Kingsmead and very little else.

A terrible weekend followed. The cupboards were all but bare by Saturday night. She borrowed some tins of beans and peas, she cadged some milk for Sunday and bought a cheap loaf of sliced bread. There was no coffee or tea. The children drank water-thinned milk with their meals and Gabrielle didn't eat at all. The children fretted constantly, bawling and fighting. Cigaretteless, empty-bellied, Gabrielle endured. She thanked fortune that this was happening in early summer. In winter, that weekend would have been insurmountable.

'When I took the cheque up to the bank in Finsbury Park, I was off my head. I had to cash the cheque in the branch against

26

which it was drawn and I had to walk all the way from Hackney to Finsbury Park because I didn't even have the bus fare. It took more than an hour to cash the cheque. The staff were suspicious because I didn't have a bank account. They demanded lots of proof of identity but weren't happy with the different kinds of ID that I showed them. They rang the agency who'd given me the cheque but the boss wasn't there and they told the bank that they'd call them back. I had to wait for more than an hour as everybody stared at me. I hadn't eaten since Saturday afternoon and Jack and Mary hadn't had any breakfast and they were whining on at me. I started crying. It was so humiliating. I was so tired. I'd never been treated like this before. By the time they gave me the money, I couldn't have cared less.'

I had heard a litany of pitfalls, disasters and crises from Gabrielle. She'd been deserted, robbed, beaten, raped, cheated and humiliated. Of all of that, I think the episode that depressed me most was the way she had been treated in the bank. We have all had our small-scale embarrassments and trials in banks – they can be alienating and distressing beyond measure. With the aggregate of misery which Gabrielle had just endured, her dealings with the bank seemed such a wanton humiliation, such an absurd and pointless assault on her remaining dignity.

'What amazed me,' Gabrielle told me, 'and this is what I worked out in the bank – what amazed me was that I could be destitute so fast. In about a month I had gone from a nice flat with nice things and a husband earning a good wage, to living in this dump with the kids without enough money even to feed us properly. When it was all actually happening, I was too stunned to really see what was going on. I just thought about Tony coming back. After what he did to me when he came back, I was just numb. He must hate me, I thought. He must really just hate me. Then I thought . . . he must have hated me for ages. It would've been a different story if I'd been the man. Then *I* could have left the kids behind and taken all the money. But I wouldn't have been able to do something like that. How could he have done it, then? I try to put myself in his shoes . . . but it's impossible.'

She told me that she had found strength in blaming Tony entirely for what had happened to her and her children.

'At first, you always get this thought in your head that it might be your fault – that you might have been doing something wrong. That's bad – it stops you acting. I'm not fucking inadequate. *He* left *us*. He took *our* money. I mean, he's not stupid. He knew what he was doing. He went ahead and did it anyway. It makes you wonder about men – it makes you wonder if there's any good in them at all.'

She walked into the kitchen abruptly and switched her kettle on. She called out to me, asking if I wanted more coffee. I said that I did. I followed her into the kitchen, carrying both cups. I found her laughing.

'You know,' she said, 'the best of it was that I thought I was a real victim, I thought that people would break down and cry when I told them my story. I thought the DSS would be beside themselves and they'd give me everything I deserved.' She cackled outright this time. 'You've got to be joking. When they were told what had happened they more or less said it was my fault. I'd married him, hadn't I? It was me that had made the big mistake. Me and my kids were going to have to pay for that. I should've known what he was like.'

The kettle clicked and she busied herself with coffee-making.

'Yeah. In the end it was all my fault. I should've known. I should've had a crystal ball that was going to tell me what a bastard he was going to be. How can any woman tell how a man is going to turn out when they're such animals? They speak a different language. Lies, that's their language. How can you know what they're going to become?'

I looked closely at Gabrielle over the rim of my cup. Ashamed, I tried to look like something other than a man. I mumbled something neutrally upbeat and witless. She smiled kindly.

*

In the following couple of weeks I spent much of my time with Gabrielle. Her circumstances had been so extreme and critical that there was still a multitude of entitlements which she had not received. Though her husband had left her, stolen some of her property, assaulted and threatened her; though Tony had done all this, Gabrielle had neglected to take out either a separation or a maintenance order. Her benefit claims had not been well organized or consistently fought for. Living in a flat for which she could not claim Housing Benefit was foolish. She could not afford to pay any rent out of the benefit meant to sustain her and her children's daily costs. The letting agency which had defrauded her remained unmolested.

That Gabrielle had neglected to pursue so many of her rights and entitlements was predictable. Such failure is widespread. It is a factor in the formula of deprivation which many sympathetic commentators are uncomfortable with. It leads to ethical qualms about advocacy. Anyone with any experience of dealing with any branch of social services will know that claimants/clients *always* receive fairer treatment after the intervention of an educated, middle-class advocate, professional or voluntary. This is fact, not opinion – mine or anyone else's.

It's a murky issue, advocacy. It's smudged by both right and left into their own shapes and colours. Some people use it as a moral stick with which to further belabour the poor. Standing under the banner of righteous self-help, the bullish among us pour scorn upon the competence of the deprived since they seem so incapable of helping themselves by themselves. The advocacy issue makes them seem passive and inadequate and therefore less deserving of aid, financial or otherwise.

This is a flimsy and wicked notion for a number of reasons. The middle-class pundits who promote it would themselves be all awash with confusion if they lost their own little armies of advocates, their solicitors, their accountants, their counsellors and acolytes. The sheer complexity of the procedures which the poor must undergo would astonish the bourgeois. Have you ever seen an Income Support application form? Now, I read

English at Cambridge University and this document bewildered me. These things are two-volume nightmares, they are *War and Peace* in the original Russian, they're Braille to the sighted, they're impenetrable.

Additionally, those who tend to claim benefit and most particularly, emergency payments of any kind, are likely to be desperate. Exhausted, demoralized, hungry, suffering appalling stress. They are likely to be poorly educated and lacking confidence in dealing with the shoddy authority of bureaucracy. This is not a condition in which to conduct any dealings with competence. No allowance is made for this. Benevolent advice is rarely given. Men and women sit in benefit offices for hours. Workless and desperate men, mothers with hungry children, families threatened with eviction or worse.

Whatever any expert, minister or commentator says, the DSS does not attempt to ease the plight of its claimants. (Its customers, its clients, its employers.) At many turns in the claimant's labyrinth, the merest guiding word could help enormously, provide a massive shortcut through the humiliation and shame of the hours or days they have to wait in squalid, demoralizing rooms. I met no one who had enjoyed such guidance. The universal tale was obstruction, incompetence, contempt and wilfulness from DSS officials. Even if you believe that the poor are inveterate, whingeing con-men, it's impossible to ignore the weight of unanimity here. Those state agencies that deal with the poorest of the population pursue working practices that would be considered barbaric and intolerable by any other section of the community. It wouldn't happen in Knightsbridge. Cheltenham wouldn't stand for it.

And, of course, try doing whatever you do without a telephone. Try doing it when a book of stamps is a major budgeting problem. Try keeping calm with an insolent bureaucrat telling you why you can't feed your children for the next week. Try keeping calm with *anyone* who has kept you waiting for four or five hours. Could you manage it? I couldn't. There'd be fisticuffs, litigation, gunplay.

★

So, is it then laudable to advocate on behalf of claimants? Many of those who work in this field, professional and voluntary, find themselves confused about the moral imperatives of their work. It can seem patronizing, a further assault on the self-determination and dignity of the poor. It does not tackle the underlying problems of their deprivation and outsidership. It doesn't seem right.

I didn't advocate on Gabrielle's behalf. There was a set of measures that she could take to improve her conditions. We discussed these. I was only an ear for her worries, a sounding board. She took those steps herself. She contacted a legal aid solicitor. She got her separation order and her maintenance order. She wrote a letter to the DSS concerning her benefit claim. The solicitor wrote to the infamous letting agency, threatening litigation if the remainder of Gabrielle's money wasn't immediately returned to her.

These actions produced real changes. Gabrielle was liberated by the sudden realization that ostensibly these agencies were there for her benefit. She was basically their employer. If she took them at their word and persistently and skilfully demanded the rights that they themselves claimed to be hers then she could only prevail. The sensation of freedom and enfranchisement that Gabrielle felt was considerable. Choice, the least of the poor's possessions, was hers. She was victor not victim. Though the various battles she was beginning to win would not make her prosperous, they did allow crucial opportunities for choice and action.

Gabrielle invited me to dinner to celebrate the resolution of her most immediate difficulties. She had received the remainder of the money that the letting agency had owed her. She served some kind of badly cooked complicated chicken dish. I brought some bad wine. We enjoyed ourselves. I was more than pleased to see her so buoyant. It felt strange to have my knees under such an elegant spread, while outside Kingsmead rumbled and fulminated in its grime and dislocation. I was sitting in a high-rise flat with an unemployed single mother in an area of mythical deprivation. I felt near the centre of things. Gabrielle spoke.

'This is going to be the worst bit,' she said.

I was stunned. It showed, obviously. Gabrielle smiled and explained.

'Well, when things were really, really bad, you could occupy yourself by trying to sort the whole mess out. It gave you a reason to get up in the morning. You could put off thinking about the worst thing of all – the future.'

She poured the last of the wine into her own glass and looked at me. Gabrielle had a disconcerting knack of writing herself.

'I mean, what am I going to do now? It was all a big crisis before, but now me and my kids are going to have to sort out how we're gonna live our lives for the next few years. The problems are only starting now. There are lots of them and those are only the ones I can think of *now* – what about the ones that will surprise me? After all the shit and bother of the past few months, you'd think I'd deserve a break or a bit of good luck. I'm not going to get it. I'm going to have to run faster than I can just to stay still.'

This was not what I wanted to hear. My glow of satisfaction faded. I had fantasized, concocted a picture of Gabrielle, five years hence in the same position, still grateful for the break that she had just made. I realized that this was ridiculous and disgusting. Gabrielle wanted self-sufficiency, a measure of prosperity for her children. She wanted out of Kingsmead. She wanted progress and change for her family. I had imagined her to be satisfied with a situation that I myself would never have tolerated. I had been guilty of all the sophistries that I most despised.

*

Over the next few days, Gabrielle addressed herself to her housing problem. She was in a dilemma. It appeared that it was difficult to approach the council for help while living in a council flat illegally sub-let from its proper tenant. If she approached the council looking for accommodation she would jeopardize her present accommodation. The likely reaction from the council would be to evict her. She would then be stuck in a decrepit bed and breakfast hotel while she worked her way through the council's sluggish priority housing list. This didn't appeal, predictably.

I could offer no real help with this and the time had come for me to move on. I had met up with Donovan again and we had decided to spend some time together, seeing what we could see. I had spent only a few weeks with Gabrielle but I had grown fond of her. She had been unfailingly kind and generous to me. She had given her time uncomplainingly. At times she seemed more passionately committed to my work than myself. She had been strong, bright and clever.

I spent the day before I proposed to move on with Gabrielle and the children. I made lunch. Gabrielle's cooking was terrible. It was the most feminist thing about her. Her cooking was beyond politics. Gabrielle sat at the much-scuffed kitchen table watching me. She spoke of suddenly realizing that she was finally separated from her husband. It was entirely finished. Pot in hand, I asked her how she would deal with this solitude in addition to all her other problems.

'The kids,' she replied. 'The kids are going to be enough to keep me going for the minute. For always. I'll always have enough love in my life with them around.'

An astoundingly beautiful thing to say. As with most of what Gabrielle said, this caused the old mixture of edification and shame. It felt false to be leaving her so that I might stick to some flimsy hack's timetable. My role caused me uneasiness again, voyeur, dilettante. My notebook and my midget recorder had interfered all along. Gabrielle had been round and real and vivid. I had been half a man.

Gabrielle was outraged when I mentioned this. She disagreed completely (thank God).

'The second or third day you were here,' she said, 'you told me that you wanted to see an eviction . . . you were desperate. [This is true. I was obsessed with writing a good eviction scene. I almost advertised for one.] You remember that? Last week there was an eviction just across the road. I could see it from the window. You and Jack were playing on the floor with his Etch-a-Sketch. I told you about the eviction and you ignored me. You just went on playing with Jack. You didn't even bother to come to the window and have a look.'

Gabrielle's smile was triumphant. I didn't remember the incident of which she spoke. I remembered the Etch-a-Sketch (mostly for Jack's scorn at my own attempts) but I recalled no eviction. I wondered briefly if Gabrielle had made it up to make me feel better. I doubted it. I was encouraged. I probably hadn't heard her. It wasn't a moment of integrity or great self-denial but perhaps not hearing was a good enough sign in itself.

When I walked away from Gabrielle's flat that night I was glad to be gone. I wasn't working hard enough – I was behind already. Gabrielle had become a friend and therefore not a booksworth of poverty. The largest part of what she had taught me was that being poor is bad enough, but being a poor woman is worse. Gabrielle's gender had hammered her harder than any other factor. She had plummeted from her average prosperity to total collapse mostly because she was female. When she had given birth to Mary, her husband had been adamant that she should never work again. From then on Gabrielle had been dependent and vulnerable. Even if Tony had been the total husband, pacific, tender and supportive, Gabrielle was vulnerable. Her continuing stability depended on the whim of a man. Most housewives are at the mercy of this same whim. Many women are economically dependent on their husbands and the threat of being left helpless is always there. I couldn't live like that.

As it happened, I saw Gabrielle again within the month. She

was to re-enter my life in an unexpectedly dramatic way. I was soon to be back in Kingsmead, gratefully embroiled in Gabrielle's history once again.

For the moment though, I walked away happily enough. Kingsmead was dark, frightening and exciting. I was cut loose in Hackney once again. I was eyes forward within its battered streets and grimy charm, seeking the spectacle of waste and the rest of its predictable guest list.

FOUR

One of the most lunatic commentaries on deprivation was made when Channel 4 News commissioned a series of three different reports on poverty in Britain from three academic 'experts' in the field. In one of the short films, a bellicose American professor took a camera crew into the Gorbals. His main thesis was that the people who lived there weren't poor, because their homes were clean and decent, their children were clean and decent and they themselves were more than presentable. I was appalled. This man, whose opinions had influence and whose notions were thought eminent, was denying the evident deprivation of an entire community simply because that community wasn't dirty enough for him. He needed squalor as evidence of hardship. The myth that the poor necessarily live in squalor is groundless but tenacious. It survives and endures.

In the north of England, in Wales, Scotland and Northern Ireland, a different cliché predominates – that the poor are disproportionately, obsessively hygienic. The picture painted is of the working-class woman, all headscarf and slippers, spending an hour a day on her knees polishing the whitewashed front step. I myself underwent a childhood of sometimes riotous hardship but I didn't see a grimy wall or a dirty rug until I met some middle-class people.

During the time I spent in Hackney, I was continually surprised by people's readiness to talk to me, to accept me, to tell me about their lives and invite me into their homes. The latter was particularly unexpected. The graciousness and courtesy with which Hackney people asked me in was remarkable. The

English can be funny about who they let into their house. It is the very centre of their lives. I don't want to hammer the middle class (the middle class are OK by me), but as I sat in strangers' kitchens and parlours, I couldn't help thinking that I wouldn't have received such warmth and openness in suburbia.

I did see squalor in Hackney. Many of the squats were terribly dirty, some dangerously so. Some privately rented accommodation was so structurally fucked that cleanliness would have been impossible anyway. However, my overriding experience was that the homes I saw were scrupulously clean and tidy. Most were cheaply furnished and sparsely kitted out for living but their condition was largely impeccable. I don't know why it should amaze me so. Cleanliness isn't particularly expensive. Water is cheap, though soap, washing-up liquid and detergents are serious claims on limited budgets. It is the priority given to hygiene and order by people baited and chafed by poverty that is unexpected and revealing. With the multiple stresses and preoccupations resulting from poverty, hygiene seems like the last thing you'd worry about.

I saw so many homes in Hackney that I feel I can make general comments that I would not otherwise risk. The following is a summary of general notes I made about the interiors I saw.

The homes were universally too small. Particularly when occupied by families with children, the space available was terribly inadequate. Obviously, the larger the family the greater the strain. There were examples beyond number of families of five or more occupying accommodation intended for single- or two-person occupancy. It's nothing new, of course. Indeed, it used to be worse. My own childhood was spent in houses of Lilliputian dimensions. I've never understood the old apothegm that what seems big to you as a child is always puny later in life. Things always seemed pretty minuscule when I was a kid.

Bedrooms were especially inadequate. A Catch-22 situation

operated with bedrooms. The more you had, the smaller they were. No matter what the number of bedrooms were, the *actual* sleeping space never seemed to increase. For some reason, it was the bedrooms that seemed particularly prone to damp. Perhaps this was due to the type of heating that had to be improvised in these rooms (depressingly few homes had central heating). I don't know much about two-bar electric heaters or SuperSers but they seem to cause real grief for walls. I saw bedroom walls so mouldy that they looked like mushroom farms. Pulmonary complaints were rife, predominantly in the children: asthma, bronchitis, chest infections. Some of the adults rumbled and bubbled with emphysema.

Several families were compelled to make one or more family members sleep in the sitting room on sofas, camp-beds or in sleeping bags stretched on the floor. In one Dalston home, the parents of a large family shared one bedroom with their youngest child; another bedroom was occupied by the next youngest pair – nine-year-old twin brothers; two teenage daughters slept in the sitting room, alternating use of the sofa every other night; the eldest boy, a twenty-year-old unemployed youth, slept in the kitchen, underneath the kitchen table.

The kitchens I saw in Hackney were variable in size, condition and utility. Some left me frankly covetous while others, sometimes in otherwise decent homes, still managed to be a disgrace. Again there tended to be very little space. (Does someone think poor people are much shorter and thinner than other people?) Consumer durables were rudimentary or invisible. In nearly sixty homes, I saw *three* washing machines and a surprising paucity of fridges. I sat in around ten kitchens that had no fridge. Most of the cookers were five years old or older and most had some kind of mechanical grievance. Cupboard space was routinely poor – with the kind of food stocks that these people had, cupboard space didn't have to be great. Sometimes the kitchen sinks were tiny, temperamental or completely clapped out. I met two families who had to use bathroom sinks for kitchen use.

Man, Whitechapel

Morning, Bromley-by-Bow

Bus-stop, East Ham

Low-paid worker, Hackney

Low-paid worker, Paddington

Closing, Whitechapel

Evening, Petticoat Lane

High-class tailors, Aldgate

Janitor, Commercial Road

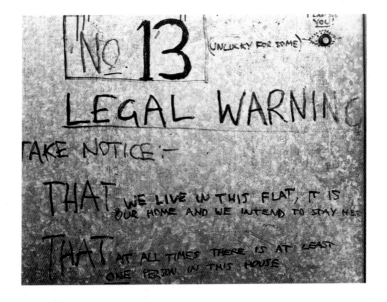

Squatter's notice, Hackney

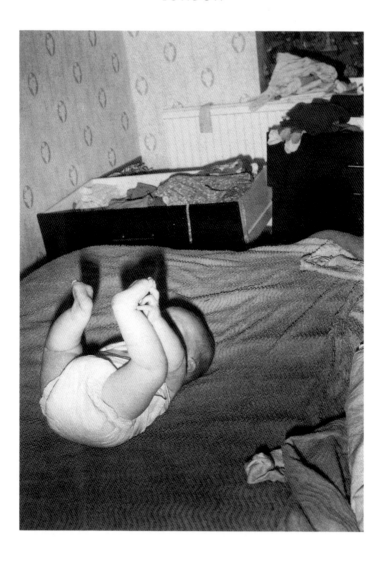

Infant, Hackney Downs

Top: *Mother and daughter – Graham Road squat, Hackney*

Bottom: *Bathroom – Graham Road squat, Hackney*

Gas works, Vauxhall

Foraging, Whitechapel

Street party, Petticoat Lane

Dustcart, Bromley-by-Bow

6.00 p.m., Entrance, St Botolph's

6.30 p.m., outside St Botolph's

Homeless woman, St Botolph's

Seamus, St Botolph's

Alan Grant, St Botolph's

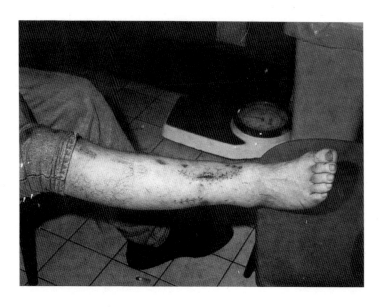

Peter's leg, St Botolph's

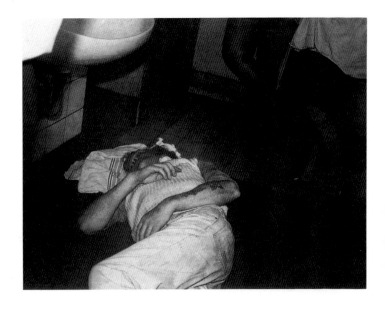

Overdose, St Botolph's

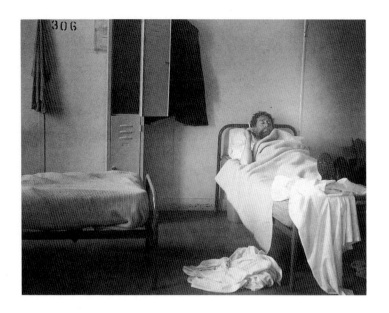

Tooley Street Hostel

Sleeping out, Lincoln's Inn Fields

Victor James Huxtable at home, Mile End Road

Victor James Huxtable at work, Whitechapel Methodist Mission

Regulars, Whitechapel Methodist Mission

Pool hall, East Ham

Bedroom, Tooley Street

Mrs Worrel, St Botolph's

Worrel children, c. 1960

It is difficult to imagine the extra difficulties faced by a family with poor kitchen facilities. It costs more to have a bad kitchen. You can't cook a large meal and freeze it for later if your freezer is knackered or if you don't have one at all. Old fridges are more expensive to run and food spoils faster. Bills can burgeon uncontrollably. In addition, a family with more than two children struggles badly without a washing machine. Launderettes are no real substitute. They can be expensive, they're time-consuming and frequently dangerous. Single mothers, in particular, are at the mercy of their kitchens. Perishable children's foodstuffs and their mounting piles of dirty clothing can be a nightmare. Few single mothers are in a position to visit a launderette much more than once a fortnight and most have to do the bulk of their laundry by hand. People such as single mothers are constantly expected to justify their state benefits by unyielding efforts at self-help. I'm confused as to how exactly they are expected to pursue this chimera in such circumstances.

Bathrooms were among the strongest features in the most modest accommodation. Habitually cowed tenants tended to be uncharacteristically firm in demanding repairs to bathrooms and toilets. As with the prevalent cleanliness, this vigorous insistence on good bathroom and toilet standards said much about the limits of what people were prepared to tolerate. Again, it was really only squats that had appalling sanitation.

. . . A squat near the Balls Pond Road where Donovan and I drank beer with the *eight* occupants. We warbled nervously as one of the women began to breastfeed her child. Donovan pressed his thighs together and beckoned to me. An hour later on the street he told me that he was trying to get out because he needed to urinate. In photographing around the squat he had seen their toilet. Donovan said that he'd rather have pissed in his trousers than risk that facility.

Bathroom facilities were better in rented houses, both private and council. In homes otherwise decrepit and near uninhabitable, bathrooms were mostly tolerable, if uniformly tiny, and repairs meant lengthy waiting lists. The emphasis given to washing and toilet facilities in even the very inadequate homes led me to suspect that it was these families' very proximity to conditions associated with squalor that made them fight for these rights so tenaciously. It seemed an almost visible proof of dignity, reinforcement of selfhood in the face of all that they endured.

Televisions were almost universal. Only two homes, both occupied by single male pensioners, were without a television set. This is a phenomenon that is much criticized. If they're so poor how come they have televisions? It's like the smoking controversy – 'How can they afford to smoke?' Televisions, like cigarettes, seem frivolous, unnecessary luxuries. The less well off find themselves in the queasy position of having their spending habits morally endorsed or criticized by a censorious public. Television sets are regarded as definitely unnecessary for the poor.

In fact, television is *most* necessary for the poor. It is often the only form of recreation that an impoverished family can realistically share. Theatre, cinema and concerts are prohibitively expensive even with cosmetic concessions for the unemployed. Holidays and outings are out of the question. Opportunity for the family to relax together is predominantly provided by watching television together. Subsequently, the importance of a television set becomes much more immediate and paramount than in any more prosperous home where other forms of recreation might be available. In addition, the distraction that a television provides for young children who are perhaps kept indoors because of parents' fears about the safety of their area is vital, almost sanity-preserving. Television is sometimes the only facility that makes such virtual imprisonment tolerable.

Anyway, why are those with meagre resources any less entitled to enjoy something that the overwhelming percentage of the population see as their right?

Unremarkably perhaps, only two households had a telephone. Some might not consider this a tragedy. In truth, when compared with some of the routine deprivations every household was prone to, the lack of a telephone seemed a fairly minor dispossession. I mentioned this lack of private telephones to someone I knew. 'Jesus, what do they want with telephones?' he asked.

Well, I imagine that 'they' would want what the rest of us are afforded by our telephones. That is to say, access to a form of modern communication that has been rendered indispensable by its prevalence. The services that a private telephone provides naturally apply to those on low income as well. Dealing with official agencies – the DSS, the local authority, health visitors, social workers etc., would be much easier with a private telephone. The jobless are castigated for their supposed lack of effort in trying to find a job. Can you imagine how much more difficult job-hunting must be without regular access to a telephone? In deprived areas, public telephones are generally out of order – vandalized or simply neglected. In low-paid jobs, speed of application is all (first come, first served) and it would seem that a telephone would be essential to good job-hunting.

Contact with the extended family (an honoured right for the bourgeois) is difficult without a telephone. Poor families are often separated by arbitrary housing allocations, or wholesale migrations to another town or region in search of work. Families with one or more children struggle particularly without a telephone. The abrupt medical crises commonplace in a family of young children are nightmarish without one. Contact with the armies of compulsory carers, like health visitors, or schools or nurseries is enormously difficult. What middle-class mother would tolerate raising her brood without the aid of friend telephone?

And that's just the problems with out-going calls. But for out-going calls, there's always a public telephone somewhere, even if you have to travel far. The inability to take incoming calls is as, if not more, grave. Family members who are late cannot telephone to reassure anxious relatives. All the above agencies cannot contact their claimants/clients. Emergency situations cause big trouble.

How many telephone calls do you think you make in an average day? How many calls do you receive? For a week I monitored my own telephone traffic. I averaged seven incoming calls a day and made five or six out-going calls. I tried to quantify the difficulties I would have faced without my own telephone. I would almost certainly have missed the opportunity to earn one quite substantial sum of money. Several crucial issues concerning my work would have been complicated to the point of impossibility. I could not have arranged several meetings. I could not have rearranged an important appointment at very short notice. I would have drifted apart from friends who live at some distance from my own home.

Imagine how much more difficult your dealings, personal and public, would be without your telephone. Think how harassed and bothered you'd be, running along the infuriating relay of broken, pissed-on cubicles that any search for a phonebox now warrants. Imagine how much longer your life would take.

I saw so many interiors that I began to feel like a sweaty hack writing for *Good Housekeeping* or *World of Interiors* or something like that. Many passed in a blur of comparison and polemical note-taking but, just occasionally, I'd have time to think about the dimensions of someone spending their life in a home like one of these. I've lived in enough crappy boxes, enough vertiginous slivers of flat-blocks and council estates made of cardboard and glue, to know that it can make all the difference there is to make. Squeezed, cramped, chilled, damped out; men, women and children are warped and unshaped by their conditions. Some bear it well. Some build lives and surroundings of comfort or even frugal elegance. Some find their lives and their selfhoods unravelling completely.

I remember a young couple in a block of flats peppered with steel doors and metal grilles. They had reoccupied their own squat a week before. Their home was in dire condition. They had had a cooking fire about a month ago and the walls of most rooms were black or brown from smoke. Their furniture was battered, ripped and, suspiciously, loathsomely damp. Notwithstanding the gloom, grime and sordidness, the two occupants seemed to glow with excess health and cleanliness. They were bright in that dark.

. . . The towering squat behind Euston with the man with the albino ferret (which Donovan thought was a hamster). The scaled-down apartment in which Mumtaz, his wife, his mother and his three children lived, some undoubtedly sleeping in the cupboards. Old Joe S., ex-glazier, carpenter, shopfitter, welder, gardener; a thankful Joe-of-all-trades, putting new glass in his window frames once a fortnight in Nightingale. Steve and Sheila crouched over their fumy SuperSer, their faces picked out rufously in that glow, their cold meal lying on plates at their feet, thinking up ambitious plans with which to get their electricity reconnected.

This is where Donovan's photographs score heavily. It takes a better writer than I to describe the way these homes looked.

Conditions were just wrong. They were bad, dreadful, disgraceful – take your pick. *And* they were getting and are getting worse. There is a wealth of recent legislation designed to circumvent and damage the poor. The list is endless, social security 'reforms' (just love that doublespeak), Fair Rents Act abolition or castration, poll tax, benefit rule changes, savage cuts in council-house building etc. Many of these punitive swipes fall squarely on housing. The poor are being hit in their fundamental spot, where and how they live.

Areas like Hackney are forced to endure the particular opprobrium of central legislature. They are punished for being poor. They are further punished for electing predominantly Labour councils. They are surcharged, ratecapped, unsafety-netted.

Hackney is being ignored, hounded, destabilized, gentrified, underfunded, gerrymandered and disenfranchised. Its slice of the pie is getting smaller every year. Hackney is being wound down and its people are getting poorer and poorer. I'd never seen anywhere like Hackney.

FIVE

Donovan and I had split up a couple of weeks after arriving in London. After Hackney, I felt that it was time we rejoined forces. When I found him again, he had been spending the previous fortnight in St Botolph's Crypt Centre, a day and night centre for single homeless people, situated in the crypt of St Botolph's church in Aldgate. He was keen that I too should spend some time there.

St Botolph's church is situated next door to Aldgate underground station. There has been a church on the site for more than a thousand years. It is a curious location. On the border of London's financial district, the church stands on a little isthmus of pavement jutting into a tangled system of roads and roundabouts. The church itself is pretty, a combination of almost rural charm and metropolitan *élan*.

The Crypt Centre, a subterranean series of chambers, halls and archways, is a drop-in centre for the homeless. It was run by five full-time social workers, headed by Daly Maxwell, a likeable Ulsterman from Castlereagh. There was also a staff of part-time unpaid volunteers. Some of the volunteers were on placement at the Crypt, Training Employment and Church Army, but most had been recruited by advertisement. The Crypt advertised for volunteers in polytechnics, libraries, wine bars, *New Statesman & Society* and *Time Out*.

Among the aims and objectives of the Crypt Centre was a concentration on clients' housing needs with advice and support as a means of meeting those needs. The Centre also aimed to participate in housing and welfare rights campaign work and in increasing awareness of homelessness and eradicating prejudice against it.

The Evening Centre opened Monday to Thursday between 6.00 p.m. and 8.00 p.m. Drink was banned. It aimed to offer 'food, human companionship, crisis intervention support, housing advice, medical facilities, washing facilities and support from various statutory services'. It was always packed – more than a hundred indigent men and women every night. Food was handed to people as they came in the door, sandwiches labelled crudely as MEAT, FISH, SPAM, SALAD, etc. Hot food was cooked in the kitchens by a selection of ex-clients who had become volunteers.

The people who came to Botolph's were predominantly homeless. Most did the rounds of London's other shelters and hostels. The age range was enormous, from teenagers to pensioners, but the vast majority of Botolph's clients, for the Evening Centre at least, were male. Some people were sleeping out, either intermittently or regularly. Some slept in hostels or assisted housing schemes, some (particularly women) were in DSS bed and breakfast hotels. Addiction was common, whether to alcohol or to proscribed drugs, and several people were obviously mentally ill, one or two seriously so. Yet for all the similarities in their predicament, Botolph's clients were as various and individual as in any large group of people.

Daly Maxwell told me that he had been at Botolph's for eight years. 'It's the tip of the iceberg here. The people who come here or who visit similar facilities are a tiny proportion of the people who need our help or support. Basically, we try to help anyone who comes to us. The best way of doing that is to find them somewhere to live, obviously. We can't always do that. We try to co-ordinate with housing officers and with housing associations but much of the time we're compelled simply to find people places in temporary hostel dormitories just to solve their immediate difficulties, to try and get them off the street, if you like.

'But we try to look deeper and further ahead than that. We

try to encourage people to take stock of their situation and show them the possibilities for solving other problems. Many of the people we see are addicted to alcohol or drugs and, obviously, that's something we have to address – help the people themselves to confront.

'I think a lot of people would consider the people that come here as beyond help or unworthy of help. That's just not true. We can't achieve miracles. Our resources are limited but if we can alleviate someone's difficulties in some way, big or small, then the whole thing's worth it.'

The Centre is, as I've said, on Church property; it is jointly financed by Church of England fund-raising and the DSS. Indeed, the nominal overseer of the Centre was a cleric. However, there is no emphasis on the Church or religion. The place was a pragmatic attempt at alleviating certain empirical social difficulties. Organized religion has historically been associated with some unfortunate attempts at intervention in poverty relief. Force-fed prayers over soup-kitchen meals are not long gone. St Botolph's is certainly an improvement on that.

Donovan and I helped out for a time. It was uncomfortable work. I had been homeless as a very young man and it was distinctly odd to see a place like Botolph's from the other end. Much of what we did felt bad. I didn't like standing behind a table at the front door, handing people food as they came in: there was a lack of dignity in the process that could easily have been avoided. The other volunteers behind the tables would greet entrants with the words 'Meat, fish, Spam,' indicating the type of rolls or sandwiches on offer. Repeated over and over again, it was a demeaning mantra, reminding the people coming in exactly what their position was. I brought this point up at one of the 'briefings' that volunteers and staff held in the evening. It was decided that volunteers on the door should adopt a policy of greeting people when they came in. I suppose it was good that the thing was dealt with but it seemed an artificial way to find the words, 'Hello' or 'How are you?' Perhaps it was one of Botolph's definitive problems, which it shares with all such

Centres, that such behaviour was not the natural impulse of all who worked there.

I liked many of the people who visited Botolph's. I disliked some too. Donovan was slightly shocked by this at first, as though one had to like all poor people. Such a notion is the most crass kind of bourgeois sentimentality. People who are poor are as multiple and complex as any others and just as worthy of like and dislike.

People told me terrible stories: of some dreadful collapse in their life, a home broken, a family bitterly separated. Some didn't have to tell their stories: they were visible enough in their figures and faces, in the way they walked and spoke. Botolph's was at the extreme end of deprivation. The people there were marked and damaged by want to an extent difficult to believe.

One young woman, 'Florence', was demonstrably, acutely schizophrenic. She had recently been compelled to leave a hostel on Providence Road and was again homeless. She had managed to find another place with the Simon Community. I understood, however, that Florence's illness meant that she could rarely manage to stay in a particular hostel for any length of time. She was too difficult to cope with and hostels generally ejected her, claiming that her presence upset the other residents.

Florence was very ill indeed. Whenever I spoke to her, she was always tense and excited. She told me that she had seen people sneaking up on her while she was asleep, frightening her and making her 'think of things'. One afternoon Florence continually slipped away and changed into an ever more bewildering variety of different outfits which she had just commandeered from Botolph's stock of donated clothing. She had decided that she wanted to be a nun and spoke at length about how much she looked forward to taking holy vows. She was disturbed that despite her religious intentions, many of the 'things' which she was compelled to think were violent. She told me of fantasies of murder and vengeance upon people she barely knew.

Schizophrenia is a devastating illness. Florence was gravely disturbed. She should not have been in Botolph's. The other clients were brutally careless of her plight. They were rude and dismissive. Some even teased her. It was, manifestly, not a suitable environment. Daly Maxwell conceded that there was little that he or his staff could do for her.

'She should, of course, be receiving proper psychiatric help – she should be an in-patient. She's too ill to cope with life on her own. But getting her seen by a GP would be an achievement, never mind getting her admitted somewhere.'

Florence was suffering some of the grossest effects of the government's policy of releasing the mentally ill 'into the community'. Many people are quite as ill and having to try to cope with life without the aid of psychiatric help but are completely incapable of doing so. As the scheme widens its scope, many more such people will be dumped 'into the community' where eventually, too ill to manage, they will end up homeless. The scheme is clearly failing disastrously as a system of care. As a system of budget-cutting it is perhaps doing rather better.

'Martin' was a young Glaswegian who was living in a squat near Euston. He had spent a year sleeping out on the streets when he first arrived in London. Like many young homeless, he had eventually graduated into occupying a squat found by some friends he had made while sleeping rough. He told me why he had left his home town.

'My da was beating me all the time. He was always on at me to get a job – he was on the dole himself but he thought that there was no excuse for me not having work. He just kept looking for excuses to have a go at me. He was a hard man. One time he broke my collar bone. It was always either me or my ma got the brunt of it. In the end he kicked me out and told me he'd kill me if I ever came back. There was nothing for me in Glasgow so I thought I'd try my luck in London. Big mistake.'

(Incidentally, I've noticed that some commentators consider the reasons that the young homeless give for leaving home footling trifles. There seems to be an idea that they should go back home. No domestic strife could be as bad as the trials of homelessness. Those who believe this must have had very nice parents indeed. The ruptures that can occur in families already torn by the stress of deprivation can be very considerable. Abuse or violence should not have to be endured by anyone. Most young homeless people don't go back home because they *cannot* go back home. Often, there is no true home to go back to.)

Martin hoped that, if he could find permanent accommodation with the aid of the staff at Botolph's, he would be able to get a better grip on his life. What he did not tell me was that he was a chronic alcoholic, though still barely twenty-one. Another man who lived in the same squat told me that Martin had started drinking when he was sleeping on the streets and that his addiction was uncontrollable.

According to Daly Maxwell, such addiction was unsurprising for people faced with the kinds of difficulties with which his clients were faced. 'When there seems to be so little hope in your situation – it's inevitable that any crutch, any aid to coping is going to be attractive. A lot of the most severely addicted people here aren't what you called "temperamentally" addicted. There *are* several who would be addicts whatever their circumstances but there are others who are addicts mainly because of their circumstances – because they have no money, no family and nowhere to live. I mean, that's enough to drive most people to drink or drugs.'

Daly's views on the people with whom he worked were always sympathetic. His experience in such work had not jaded or hardened him. He did not want 'to breastfeed the world' but he felt that, if he could identify and isolate particular problems that people had, he could work with them to find pragmatic solutions or improvements. In many ways, Daly held Botolph's together. When he was absent, the Centre could degenerate quite abruptly. One night, when he was not there, some volunteers did not turn up and there was not a full complement of staff and volunteers (that is, at least two social workers and five volunteers). A decision was taken not to open the Evening Centre fully. No one was allowed into the building. Food was handed out through doors barred by desks and even through open windows. Suddenly, Botolph's had become the worst kind of soup kitchen, the worst kind of insult. I climbed over one of the tables and went outside and sat with the disgruntled clients while they ate their brusquely doled-out meals. No volunteer nor staff member joined us outside.

In fairness to the staff at Botolph's, their time and resources are unequal to their task in many ways. Sometimes, niceties of tone have to be abandoned but, none the less, there is a latent risk in insensitivities such as the one I've described. Treatment like that can alienate the people who use the Centre and discredit or destroy some of the aims and objectives which it so proudly promotes.

Daly realized how delicate the relationship between clients and staff could be. He was keen to avoid a 'them and us' schism between the two groups. 'In some ways, I'm just as interested in the reasons the volunteers give for coming here as in the reasons the clients give. When you think about it, it's an odd thing to do. To give up your time and come down here and do this strange work. The volunteers have certain needs that they meet by coming here. The clients have needs that *they* meet by coming here. The needs might be different but it blurs the distinction between the clients and volunteers. Everybody is getting something out of this place.'

I noticed that he hadn't included the staff like himself in this cosy comparison. I challenged him about this. He laughed.

'Oh, the staff are different from the clients. There's a big difference. It's the biggest difference of all – we're being paid to be here.'

In some ways, homelessness is a distraction when considering the dimensions of poverty in a society. It represents a tiny proportion of a society's poor and involves circumstances which most deprived people do not share. Nevertheless, homelessness is much in the news these days, perhaps precisely because it *is* a distraction from the wider issues of poverty. It is also newsworthy because it has the stark dramatics of all extreme situations. It is also very *visible*. There can be no more unavoidable testament of destitution than the sight of people sleeping on the streets – though even street homelessness is a distraction from the larger dimensions of homelessness, people living in hostels, DSS hotels, squats.

But, on the other hand, the *new* homeless, the new young homeless, are evidence of something that applies to all those who live on low incomes in Britain. Everyone has noticed the sudden increase in ordinary young people, not people who would traditionally have been associated with indigence, sleeping on the streets. Benefit rule changes introduced in 1988 have made it very difficult for sixteen to eighteen year olds successfully to claim Income Support. Thus, Housing Benefit is often a practical impossibility for a young person who cannot live at home or who has been in the care of the state. These rule changes have pushed enormous numbers of disadvantaged young people into hostels and on to the streets. There can be no argument about this. Among the lists of DSS intransigence and incompetence no other cause and effect are so closely linked. There can be no argument and there can be no excuse. It is an appalling situation, which disgraces all of us, as members of a society that can do something so callous and stupid to save a few million pounds a year.

Similarly, cruel benefit changes, changes that affect all those on low income, have been common in the last decade and more. People living on state benefits have seen their living standards plunge inexorably. Many vicious tweaks have been perpetrated on the benefits system, the most deplorable, probably, the Social Fund (another euphemistic disgrace). Replacing a special payments system, which was meant to enable claimants to buy one-off items such as beds, cookers, furniture, the Social Fund is a *loans* system. If claimants receive a grant from the Social Fund, repayments are deducted from their benefit, placing further strain on what is usually an already inadequate income.

Grotesquely, Social Fund budgets are limited each year. If Social Fund managers spend their budget six months into the year, they can give no grants for the next six months. It hurts your head to think about a notion like that.

The whole system of social security payments is being fatally eroded. The whole *idea* of state benefits is being eroded. The concept 'social security' is a fascinating one. It is rich in implication and meaning. It is interesting to consider what exactly we do or did mean by it. Does it indicate that the financial security of an *entire* society, including its least wealthy, is desirable? Does it hint that a society itself is only made secure by adequate provision for its poorest members? Whatever its meaning, it is certain that current trends in social security legislation are a contradiction in terms.

The homeless endure a harsh reality of social insecurity. The isolation of homelessness is hard to describe adequately. My own experience of indigence was an experience impossible to associate with any of the other periods or parts of my life. The indigent live in a dimension remote from the one in which we live. The world is different for the homeless. It is cold, wet, dangerous, lonely and marginal. It bears little resemblance to late twentieth-century life as lived by most people in western Europe.

Perhaps homelessness is the single aspect of poverty that fiction tackles best. The revealed truth of fiction is sometimes a stronger truth than a fact too outrageous fully to comprehend. It is easy to see indigence as a phenomenon entirely removed from our own circumstances. Maybe the necessary empathy of the novel is one of the few routes to understanding such a predicament.

★

Daly Maxwell told me that, since working in Botolph's, his dominant ambition had been to avoid hurting people's feelings or pride while still helping them as best he could.

'The thing about working in this place is that I think some of those on the volunteer/staff side start thinking that they're different, maybe even better than the client. I'm always conscious of how similar a lot of my clients are to me. That's the case in everybody's life. You meet people and you find similar ground between you and you go on from there. Our clients obviously respond well to being treated as people rather than cases. And they *are* people after all. But even without that, it would damage me if I was to think that I'm different from them. I could be in their situation so easily. We could all be in their situation so easily. It's good to keep that in mind.'

SIX

On the day that I first met Alan, London's newspapers were filled with stories of the Iraqi invasion of Kuwait. St Botolph's situation, right on the verge of the city's financial district, was edifying and instructive. I overheard one doom-laden conversation between two banker types. They seemed convinced that a financial collapse on the scale of 1929 was imminent. The auspices were poor and both men were jumpy and furtive.

The Crypt also buzzed with the news. The homeless men and women exchanged international gossip, opinion and insight. Absurd though many of their assertions were, they seemed moderate and convincing in the teeth of tabloid warbling and bankers' nightmares. I sat at one of the long tables in the basement with a group of the Botolph's regulars and listened to their views. Donovan had already told me much about Alan and it was easy to pick him out among the others. His views on the Middle Eastern conflagration were urbane and sceptical amid the sensation and awe of the others.

Alan Grant was a forty-six-year-old Gloucestershire man. He was tall and lean, his face tanned and well weathered. His greying hair was thick and wiry. He had a crescent-shaped scar around his left eye, the result of a motorcycle accident of some years before. When Alan smiled, it crinkled into remarkable configurations.

Alan had been helping Donovan out in Botolph's and other places for nearly a fortnight before I met him. He told me that he was not a regular visitor at Botolph's and that he had come upon Donovan quite by chance on one of his rare appearances in the Crypt. As we spoke that first morning, Alan quickly grew mutinous on the subject of the Crypt. He criticized the Centre's ethos, working practices and personnel. Many of his comments were well judged and fair, but, after a bit, became irritating. He was intelligent, confident and more than willing to talk. He was some way short of unassuming and seemed keen that his patent intelligence should indeed be obvious. It was as though he was insisting on the differences between himself and the other people who used the facilities at Botolph's. Alan *was* different. He obviously thought himself better than them.

Alan had prepared for my arrival. He had even written his own introduction in Donovan's journal. I reproduce here in full:

ALAN'S INTRODUCTION

I am living in one room at the —— Hotel, a bed and breakfast hotel catering exclusively for homeless people and families housed there by Tower Hamlets Council. I was housed as a priority/essential case by Tower Hamlets due to my health problems. [Alan suffers from epilepsy.] As I am receiving sickness/invalidity benefit of £52.10, I am entitled to Housing Benefit to cover my rent which is approx. £100 p.w. I contribute £5.60 p.w. to my rent from my benefit. This leaves me approx. £45 for food, clothing, toiletries, etc. If I were working I would need a net wage of at least £150 p.w. to survive since I would then be responsible for the rent of £100 p.w. Also, if I was in full-time work, Tower Hamlets could reasonably argue that I was no longer priority and I might be evicted from the hotel.

In the short term, therefore, it is impossible to think of finding work.

The council has told me that I should be in my own flat within a month. Assuming that they are true to their word, I am then left with two choices with regards to finding a job. I can either take a 'dead end' job and neglect to tell my employer about my disability. Alternatively, I can spend heaven knows how long trying to find myself a decent job while making it difficult for myself by telling prospective employers about my health problems. The reality of this situation is that I am caught in a 'poverty trap' with only the prospect of continual low earnings due to no fault of my own.

I have been able to get myself out of this merry-go-round. I have the promise of permanent accommodation. But 95% of people in the same situation are unable, for many reasons, to get out of it.

In the case of hostels, possibly as many as 50% of the residents are ex-psychiatric patients or people who are unable to fend for themselves. Of the people who are sleeping rough, the biggest majority have, for whatever reason, being doing so for many years and either do not want accommodation or are considered by agencies to be beyond help.

If I were to apportion blame for this situation, I would be forced to blame successive governments and in particular the present one. They have 'watered down' the Welfare State to the extent that it now bears no resemblance to how it was when it was introduced after the war. Over the years, changes have been introduced: charges for prescriptions, dental work, opticians, etc. Free school milk has been abolished. Benefit for unemployed people under eighteen no longer exists. The list is endless. I can only conclude that if this continues and if the present government stays in power then we will eventually have no Welfare State.

Alan talked of many things, mostly autobiographical in nature. He was a mixture of outrageous candour and tight-lipped reserve on the subject of his own life. I recognized a sound editorial technique. I had never met anyone so absolutely willing to talk about themselves. Alan was already marshalling the facts into a careful chronology. He searched for details that he considered of particular interest or relevance and he presented them in a polished format. It was as though he was preparing his memoirs. I began to feel like a ghost writer.

He told me that he had been homeless for just over three years. He was the father of four children aged between twelve and twenty-two. Alan often spoke of his ex-wife with great bitterness. He would seem to crank himself up until he felt goaded by injustice. Then he would consider himself wronged and betrayed. There were other moments which I felt were truer to him when he softened, talked more moderately and showed the extent of how hurt he had been.

Alan told me remarkable things about himself. He spoke well, his words were slow, hypnotic. Our longest exchanges took place during a series of afternoons when we sat in his bare hotel room, smoking and drinking chilled water, tense and feeble in the hard heat of that surprising summer.

After Alan left school, he had started in the probation service. (I should say that I was often confused about the details of Alan's employment history. Whether it was his vagueness or my incompetence is hard to say but I know that, much as I tried, I couldn't get a firm version.) Dissatisfied, he decided to go into social work. He studied successfully for his CQSW (a professional qualification in social work). He started working as a full-time social worker and was married to Wendy. After some years in the caring professions, he returned to Gloucestershire with his family and started working as a second-hand car salesman. He started his own car sales business. He bought a bigger house and worked feverishly to pay off the mortgage. By the late seventies, his marriage was stalling.

Alan described an almost soft-focus version of family life – bungalow, caravan on the coast, wife, kids and dog. He considered this 'a nice little lifestyle'. Its maintenance involved him working hours that his wife could not accept. The strain of his absence grew intolerable.

'The crunch came when she started divorce proceedings. Unreasonable conduct was what she cited . . . to this day, I'm convinced that it was her mother who talked her into it . . . the mother never liked me. In the end, I didn't contest it. It was pointless – that's what she expected me to do. I'm really sure that in her heart of hearts she thought that when I contested it she would have made her point and we could have forgotten all about the divorce so long as I fell in with whatever plans she had. But I figured that if her mother could talk her into it now, she could talk her into it in three years' time.'

It was 1984. Alan was divorced and he lost the house.

He was enjoying the theatre of our talks. The gloomy, cell-like basement room, the clouds of cigarette smoke suited his sluggish but authoritative voice as it rumbled into my recorder. I didn't need to ask questions. Alan spoke in thirty-minute bursts. I watched him as he spoke. He turned to me often, a professional smile on his face. I felt that as he enjoyed it more, he told me less. The events that took him from divorce to indigence raced by, seamlessly brief.

'When I got divorced, I went to stay with my mum and dad. It wasn't a good idea so I got myself a bedsit. This was bad too since I was bumping into Wendy every other day and things were getting increasingly acrimonious. So . . . I just upped and left.' Alan laughed. He looked at me and saw my smile. Encouraged, he laughed louder. 'It was easy in the end.

'I started moving around the country. I just wandered. I went everywhere south of Derby. I went to Nottingham, Coventry, Birmingham, Cirencester, Bristol, Cardiff, Swansea, Pembroke Dock, Tenby, Bridgwater, Weston-Super-Mare, Taunton, Exeter, Plymouth, Southampton, Portsmouth, Bournemouth, Poole, Swanage, Newbury, Swindon, Oxford and Reading.'

He chuckled as he concluded his improbable list. The scar on his eye bobbed roguishly. I asked him where he had stayed in all these places and for how long.

'Oh, I stayed in night shelters, hostels. I patronized a well-known national chain of park benches. God, it was amazing. There was just something in me that kept me on the move. I drove the DHSS fucking insane trying to keep up with me. I mean, half the time I didn't even bother to claim. It wasn't worth the hassle, especially if I was sleeping out at the time.'

Abruptly, Alan's flippancy ceased. His voice became much less confident and his face betrayed unease.

'What was going on in my head at that time? What was pushing me round the map like that? Well, while I was happy to be rid of Wendy in a lot of ways – in other ways, I missed being married. That sounds silly but man is not a solitary creature. I'd never really lived on my own. I'd moved from my parents' home straight into marriage with Wendy. It was difficult to accept that I was by myself and I didn't accept it . . . I wasn't accepting it. I was sleeping in parks and DHSS fleapits. I wasn't going to get up in the morning and find the dog downstairs, the car in the drive and a clean shirt and a good breakfast waiting for me. I only realized what had happened to me after it was all over.'

Alan's story was remarkable and improbable in equal measure. (Where had his car-sales business gone?) He had moved from that soft-focus suburban dream to the nightmare life of a peripatetic hobo. He actually considered rooflessness a less galling contrast with his previous prosperity than living in a flat: 'If I'd taken some kind of grotty bedsit somewhere then the comparisons would have really started. My situation would just have been a less comfortable version of what I'd had before. On the road and sleeping rough, there were just no comparisons. These were different galaxies. And, take it from me, some of the sleeping out, maybe with the exception of London, is actually less of a culture shock than some of the hostels and night shelters.'

The idea that Alan might be lying unsettled me. Some of the staff at Botolph's had poured scorn on his claims to have been a social worker. (The classic transference fantasy of the social worker's client claiming CQSWs, social work degrees, etc., is common.) I was in a peculiar position. I had a responsibility for some degree of fact and source-checking what I heard. On the other hand, I was not a journalist and thus my responsibilities as a human being were fairly serious as well. I had to treat Alan with the same respect and tact with which I would have treated anyone else. After meeting someone at a party, I wouldn't ring up all their friends the next day to ratify all I had been told the night before.

As my doubts about Alan's truthfulness increased, we spent

less time in Botolph's. Alan didn't like to meet there. He preferred, quite rightly, that we should talk when we were alone. Anyway, since many of the Alan-doubters worked there it was becoming an atmosphere destructive to any possibility of candour on his part.

We spent much time together walking the streets, in bars or in Alan's room at the hotel. Donovan joined us often. We played pool interminably and Donovan always seemed to win. His presence was sometimes a welcome relief for both Alan and me. The hours we spent in the hotel room, subjugated by Alan's grey chanting, were sometimes wearisome. Donovan's vivacity and high spirits eased the mood.

Alan spoke of the main period during which he was homeless. 'It was obvious that after so long playing the Wandering Minstrel around the provinces that sooner or later I'd end up in London. At one time, I was actually spending more time hitching lifts than actually being anywhere – spending a day or even less in each place. I couldn't take too much of that so I ended up coming to London.

'The first night I was in London, I stayed in Nutfriars, the Salvation Army place. That was horrible enough. Eighty people in a dormitory. It was disgusting. It stank beyond belief. A good fifty per cent of the people there had been long-term psychiatric patients made homeless because of the changes in the mental health legislation. It didn't matter what their condition was, they were all treated the same – badly. The food was dreadful. I mean truly dreadful. The place was dirty. There were cockroaches. All in all, it was better to sleep rough. At least that had a bit of dignity and you were less likely to get attacked by someone violently disturbed. Anyway, the next morning, I took off. I tried to find somewhere else to sleep but I couldn't get anywhere. I went to Lincoln's Inn because that was the famous place to sleep rough.

'I can actually remember the first night I went to Lincoln's Inn. I slept in the Roundhouse, the little bandstand thing in the middle of the square. I had no bedding or anything, though in the end someone gave me a blanket. It was late autumn, near winter. It was pretty cold and I suppose that was always the biggest culture shock of all. There were a lot of people there – near two hundred some nights. There were real winos but there were others as well.

'I slept cold and wet. It was raining pretty hard and it didn't take much wind to blow it in under the roof of the Roundhouse. I was frightened for the first few weeks. This was like the Broadway of the homeless and there were quite a lot of violent people there. Some of them are still there as we speak and they're still very violent and very territorial. I realized that this was it really. I was totally opting out. As far as the system is concerned you don't exist.'

I asked Alan if he had thought about his wife that night. He considered this for a moment.

'I think that was probably more when I *stopped* thinking about her.'

Alan soon made the thorough acquaintance of what he called 'the London scene'. He went to Mortimer Street Job Centre, one of the best providers of casual work in the capital. He worked in a series of casual jobs, never declaring his income, never going through the books. He worked mostly in catering jobs, enduring the poor conditions and pay for as long as he could before moving on. The period he remembered with great-est fondness was when he worked for an air-conditioning com-pany in Hanger Lane. He had bluffed a knowledge of air-conditioning and was earning a decent(ish) wage.

'About this time I met this Irish girl who I lived with for six or eight weeks.' Alan laughed boisterously. 'Oh, God alive. Hanwell, she lived. Me and one of my air-conditioning col-leagues were in a pub one night and we met these two Irish girls, both divorced. We took a load of drink back to one of these girls' flat. I slept with one of them and my mate slept with the other. In the morning, he went back to his wife but I stayed with the one I'd lumbered. I ended up staying those six or eight weeks. Twenty-five she was. I was a lucky bugger at the time. She came from Newry and had a baby son called Cornelius. You gotta be Irish to call your son something like that. Jesus, I can't even remember that girl's name.'

Alan had told me about one or two other romantic adventures that he had when ostensibly homeless. Now, there is no reason that poverty or indigence should be a disqualification from a sexual life or a sexual appetite but Alan did seem to have been an unusually successful lover in the circumstances – almost marrying a wealthy young American woman who was living in Scandinavia. Even though he had visited Botolph's only sporadically at this time, it contradicted what Daly Maxwell had told me. Daly said that Alan had been an amazing sight, sporting a huge grey beard and dirty grey hair that fell below his shoulders. It strikes me that if *I'd* been a wealthy young American woman, I mightn't quite have thrown my shoes over the moon for this.

By all accounts, Alan was fairly broken down at this time. For three years, he visited Botolph's more regularly than he concedes. Sarah, his case-worker, commented that he seemed to lack motivation and didn't display any interest in any long-term resolution of his difficulties. From what Alan had already told me about his pervasive fatalism at this time, I wasn't surprised.

Any solutions devised by the staff at Botolph's were consistently rejected. Alan felt that these were being foisted upon him in an arbitrary manner. I was told that his alcohol problem became very grave and that he had been admitted to a detox unit for chronic alcoholics in south London. Needless to say, Alan had omitted such details.

It's true that his omissions were his business but, on the other hand, he had made such a virtue out of total candour that they were hard to ignore. I tackled him about drinking as we sat in a leprous bar in Shoreditch. Donovan had been counselling me to confront this for weeks. We sat among a clutch of Shoreditch matrons, eating verminous sandwiches while Alan spoke.

'I suppose I drank badly on and off all through that homeless period. I seemed to go for months when I'd only have the odd drink and then I'd have months when I'd be permanently oblivious. It's incredible to think I could have binged like that.' He laughed. 'I seemed to have an amazing constitution. Jesus, to take all that punishment with so little ill effect is quite incredible. I'd have done well in the jungle . . . well, I'd have done well in a jungle that grew drink.'

At first, Alan had been annoyed when I broached this subject but now, as always when he had a listener, he was beginning to enjoy himself.

'I think, to be honest, that the drinking was less important than so many other things. My marriage break-up, the fact that I was alone and couldn't bear that. I really, really missed my kids and that made me so angry and destructive. I was angry with myself as much as Wendy. With stuff like that in your life, you don't need to drink to suffer – you're already pretty well fucked.'

Alan said nothing about his present drinking habits. I can only say that I never saw Alan drunk, hung over or haunted by any alcoholic's wasted phantasms. Indeed, he seemed more organized and competent than either Donovan or me for most of the time. He told me that he was trying to get his life 'back on track'. He was trying to get a housing association to give him a flat near Petticoat Lane and, with the aid of some of the Botolph's staff, he was confident of success. The Botolph's staff, particularly Sarah, worked hard on his behalf. However, I think it's fair to say that I detected if not reluctance, then certainly a feeling that their work might be wasted. They seemed confident that Alan would be given a flat of his own but sceptical about the likelihood of his maintaining tenancy for more than a few weeks. It is naïve to criticize such scepticism among professional social workers, who spend much of their working lives investing energy and resources into providing solutions and aid for people who reject or dissipate any benefit incurred. This can breed scepticism and pessimism.

None the less, even the most wary could only concede that

for the moment, Alan was energetically pursing an improvement in his circumstances. In some ways, he reminded me of Gabrielle. Both did much to dispel the myth that the dispossessed are unmotivated and incapable of self-help. And Gabrielle and Alan were not an unrepresentative sample. Many of the people I met in London were striving to fight against some of the worst results of their situations. Alan explained his new motivation and stamina thus: 'I honestly think that there comes a time – there came a point for me certainly – there comes a time when you stand back and look at your life and you find that you have no commitments and no links with anyone and that you're on your own. You're really on your own. You realize that if you don't do something about it then it's all going to stop and you're going to end up as another uncertified body that no one will claim and no one will mourn.'

Before long, Alan received some welcome news. The Toynbee Housing Association had offered him a one-bedroom flat in a small block near Petticoat Lane. Alan was euphoric. His plans quickly became grand and a detailed conversation about his ideas for décor ensued. Within a fortnight, he had the keys to this property and was preparing to move in.

He showed me round the apartment one hot afternoon. His manner was full of something touchingly close to shy pride. The flat was rather tattered and peeling but it would have needed very little to make it more than comfortable. Alan told me that a little paint and a bit of carpet would make all the difference. I was soon to leave London and it seemed appropriate that he and I should conclude thus. We had made hopelessly sanguine plans for Alan to visit Donovan and me in Belfast but this was to be the last time I saw him. Feeble in the enervating heat, we celebrated his new good fortune.

*

I've already said that homelessness can be a distraction from the true brunt of want as endured by most of the deprived. Indigence is vivid and compelling in a manner that housing estates, council flats, squats and dole offices are not. The dramas of the homeless are played out in the city's exterior. They are there for everyone to see. For those whose lives and habits keep them away from places like Hackney, homelessness, the dormitory Strand and South Bank, can all too readily seem like the whole story.

In some ways, Alan is also a distraction. His situation cannot really be blamed on any new form of legislative harassment of the poor. He would have been impoverished and roofless without any government cuts or benefit rule changes. He had suffered years of hardship caused by destructive forces and outcomes deep within his marriage and his life. His plight was not caused by legislative misrule. It was made more grave and less soluble by misrule but Alan would have been what he was anyway.

Alan was most interesting because of his apparent disqualifications for poverty. He was an intelligent, energetic, even entrepreneurial figure who seemed particularly unsuited to pennilessness. His spectacular stories demonstrate how abruptly one can be dispossessed. Like Gabrielle, Alan had been blithely acting out a pantomime of normal British family life, of which he had been robbed with cruel speed. Whatever one might suspect about his contribution to the destruction of his marriage, it cannot be denied that the circumstances into which he was forced, emotionally as much as physically, were brutal and enervating.

That he lied to me is also crucial. I *know* that Alan lied to me on several occasions. He told me things which I *knew* to be untrue. Perhaps it's cruel to write such a thing but it is the case. Anyway, the motives for such lying are more interesting than any pontifications about deceit. Why did Alan lie?

We all lie. Many of us tell autobiographical lies, life-story distortions. The causes for this type of lie are perhaps the simplest of all. They are various – ambition, vanity or even just boredom. But our most intimate autobiographical lies are told because of shame or embarrassment. We lie about those details in our lives which we find unacceptable. We prepare different drafts of things we don't like. We offer versions which reflect better upon us.

This was what Alan did. He had already spoken of his inability to accept. To accept his solitude, the loss of his children, the loss of his prosperity. There was much else that he obviously could not accept. And his lies were less to me than to himself. He knew that I disbelieved some of what he had told me. I made this clear on a number of occasions. Alan lied to Alan. There were parts of his poverty in which Alan didn't want to believe. It wasn't such a bad way of resisting poverty's assault on the self.

On that last day I spent with Alan, we talked of this more obliquely than before. I mentioned my usual anxiety about whether I was exploiting him. Of all the people I met, Alan was the most committed to the work which Donovan and I were doing, yet I was going to call him a liar in print. I confessed that I might write about him in a way that might cause him pain or anger. We sat silently in his bare, peeling flat for some moments. I couldn't gauge the extent of his unease. We both sweated in those most un-London temperatures. I was leaving London in a couple of days and I felt as though I was running out on him. Alan concluded the ethical debate.

'Just as long as what you write is the truth. There are too many people in this country who just don't believe that this is how we live. They think it's exaggeration or whingeing. I know you're concentrating on me because you think I'm intelligent and you think this might surprise some people who think you have to be thick and dirty to be poor. Just make sure that you don't make out that I'm the exception or anything like that. We've all got worth and we're all just the same as middle-class people except that at some point something went wrong in our lives to cause real collapse. The rest started out disadvantaged because of where they lived or who their parents were. They started in a state of collapse. We're just like anybody else, only mostly unlucky.'

SEVEN

In the end I didn't leave London until more than a week after I last met Alan. Things got out of hand. The merest notion of writerly objectivity or structure collapsed. Penless, undisciplined, I got involved.

The night before I was supposed to leave for Glasgow, I was staying with some friends in Islington. Donovan was already in Glasgow and, although I wasn't looking forward to Glasgow or Donovan, I was glad to be leaving London. I'd had a surfeit of the capital and its particularly metropolitan version of poverty and dislocation. Richard, my host, was talking about the other new poor – students, suddenly forced into hardship by successive grant freezes and the new student loans system. I was beginning to worry about where I'd find some undergraduates when Gabrielle telephoned. She was in tears. She asked me to go round to her flat immediately. She pleaded. I called a cab. The taxi driver wouldn't go into the estate. I walked the rest of the way.

Gabrielle's flat was in disarray. The rubble of smashed furniture was everywhere and the kitchen floor crackled and popped with broken glass. The children, Jack and Mary, were huddled together in their bed sobbing, their faces stained and puffy with hour-old tears. Gabrielle had been beaten around the face. Her jaw was swollen and out of kilter on one side, her lips were split and bulging and one of her eyes was blood-red and closing. Somebody had come and done all the bad stuff there was to do.

Gabrielle was calm, remarkably so. She told me that Tony,

68

her husband, had found out where she lived. He had just been round. He had left an hour ago after strutting his funky all over Gabrielle's features. Gabrielle's friend/landlady had been present and Gabrielle said that her presence had stopped Tony from doing anything worse. As I inspected Gabrielle's mashed-up face, I wondered exactly what 'worse' old Tony could have done – decapitation, cannibalism?

Apparently, Tony had discovered Gabrielle's whereabouts from her mother – from whom he had also found out about me. Tony had got things rather awry. He seemed to think that Gabrielle and I were having an affair. He told her that after he and his buddies took care of me, he was going to come back to Kingsmead and take the children after settling Gabrielle's hash for her.

This wasn't great news for me. I was terrified. The bold Tony seemed a bit of a handful and I didn't want any of his literary criticism. Additionally, his misapprehension meant that I was in part responsible for what had just happened to Gabrielle. Tony and I, with our different types of manhood, had sorted her out.

I started clearing up the flat while Gabrielle tried to coax the children to sleep. Her landlady chum returned and she helped me clear up. The three of us discussed what was to be done. I offered to stay the night if Gabrielle would call the police. She agreed to this but blankly refused to go to a hospital to have her injuries looked over. Her jaw was unbroken and her eye was undamaged. She didn't want to spend four hours waiting to be seen in some casualty department.

The police came after an hour or so. They were dismissive of the night's events and seemed amused by my presence. They departed with the usual exhortations to call back if there was any further trouble. Feeling a dread only partly composed of physical fear, I spent the night there.

*

Thankfully, Tony did not reappear and the four of us passed a relatively peaceful night. By the morning, Jack and Mary were perfectly happy and even rather excited by the imminence of change that they could sense over breakfast. As we ate, we had a conference. Gabrielle's face was not as livid as it had seemed the previous night and she was confident and dominant again. She had realized that as a battered mother (which, incidentally, she had been all along) she would leap to the top of any council's priority housing list. Calling the police had been a good move since she now had evidence of physical abuse. I advised that in the meantime she should go to a women's refuge. Not only would she and the children be safe there but it would also considerably advance her housing prospects. The breakfast ended in the mood of constructive, problem-solving euphoria to which I'd become accustomed in my time with Gabrielle.

The day was spent contacting social workers and refuges. We parted early that evening. A car came to take Gabrielle and the kids to the refuge. Jack and Mary hugged me tightly as they were loaded into the car. The woman who was picking Gabrielle up seemed surprised at this tender farewell to a man. It was obviously something to which her work had not accustomed her. She was perplexed and suspicious. Gabrielle was oblivious to this. She embraced me as the woman started up the car.

I felt bereft as Gabrielle and I parted for the second time. The whole business with the refuge car seemed unreal. It reminded me just how much this was a rescue. I watched the car drive away through the battered, dusty estate. I felt drained and raw. With Alan, I had always felt uneasy about the balance of power between us. It seemed weighted always in my favour and I had often felt exploitative. Gabrielle had been a different thing. With Gabrielle I had been credulous and bewildered. Sometimes, I had felt as involved and vulnerable as she – though, it has to be said, I didn't get robbed, raped or beaten.

I hung about London for a few days, waiting for Gabrielle to contact me. Eventually she telephoned. She told me that she had been promised a flat within six months. She had sorted out her benefits and someone at the refuge was advising her about crèche facilities if she wanted to work. She sounded happy and told me that she was enjoying her time with the refuge. As usual, she was full of strength and confidence. The refuge had been a lenitive for Gabrielle. Tonic or cure, it had given her Olympian confidence and self-belief. Her hopes for her children and herself were more substantial and gleaming than ever.

A suddenly abandoned mother with two young children, since we met Gabrielle had been able to alleviate the worst effects of her situation. She had successfully sorted out her legal position, her benefit entitlements and to some degree her housing problem. Her new problem would be to prevent the future poverty of her children.

In a generation when 2.5 million children live in families on Income Support, child poverty is a common predicament. In 1991 a report by the National Children's Homes claimed that one in ten children under five from families on low income goes without enough to eat *at least* once a month because parents cannot afford to buy sufficient food. The study was carried out by the Food Commission in December 1990, gathering information from 354 families with children under five throughout Britain. The report found that the average amount spent on food per person per week was £10. This constituted more than 35 per cent of a low-income family's expenditure compared with a national average of 12 per cent.

Organizations such as the Child Poverty Action Group continue to point out that it is impossible to feed, clothe or house children adequately at current benefit levels. Infant mortality among the poor continues at an alarming rate, much higher than that for the rest of the population. It is true that the government's much-vaunted Children's Act is intended to ameliorate some of the problems of children generally and of disadvantaged children in particular. One area of especial emphasis is to be those children in the care of the state, a group who are among the most crucially dispossessed and vulnerable of Britain's children. Already, however, there is much anxiety among relevant support groups, both state and voluntary, that sufficient funding will not be available to implement some of the Children's Act's laudable aims. It was ever thus.

Poor children suffer a number of disadvantages avoided by the wider community. Their access to education, a most crucial resource for all children, is drastically curtailed when compared with the children of more prosperous parents. In particular, it might be argued that the comprehensive system has failed children from low-income families. Apart from the single example of education, the pressures on poor children are the same as those on poor adults only doubled or tripled by the complete powerlessness of children. All the stresses suffered by their parents rebound more heavily upon the children.

It is impossible to foresee in what circumstances Gabrielle's children might grow up. Gabrielle was a most scrupulous parent and, like almost all the parents I met, sacrificed her own interests for the sake of her children as a matter of course. She wanted them fed, housed, clothed and educated well. She wanted such things for her children much more than she wanted them for herself. I was sure that she would work hard for Jack and Mary, that she would sacrifice and endure much on their behalf.

None the less, her children, barring some unforeseen improvement in their circumstances, would be handicapped by poverty. For Jack and Mary to achieve the merest parity with other more prosperous children, Gabrielle would have to exert herself constantly. Perhaps the children would be ignorant of their own poverty for some time (when I was a child, I thought that poverty was the general predicament of *all* children). But, however ignorant, their lives would be complicated.

I arranged my revised departure from London. I toyed with the notion of visiting Alan and seeing how he was faring. I didn't. I was way too tired and much too unhappy by that stage. Like Hally, I just wanted to go to bed and pull the heavy covers over my head. London had wiped me out, goaded me good.

I'd had my fill of stricken people and their afflictions. I'd had enough of their anguish and endurance and enough of their fatalism.

I had spent too many months in parts of London chosen because they were poor. Fatalism was abundant there. Adversity brings its own mitigation. That palliative is often resignation of hope. To the poor, it can often seem that all the indicators in their life point downwards. Recently, the only shift in their condition has been deterioration. It corresponds to the dictum they know best – what can't be endured always gets worse. In the face of such evidence, of the damning testimony of their everyday lives, fatalism seems the only truly cogent response.

This despair chafes and festers. The idea that the reality of your life may be an irrevocable slide into deeper and greater want can lead to fantasy, to impossible pipe dreams of future prosperity. I heard many fantastic, upsetting descriptions of people's future plans to improve their incomes. Alan was going to start selling cars again. With £150 to start with, he could buy some old banger, fix it up a bit and sell it for £300. With the three hundred, he would buy two more jalopies which he could then sell for six hundred and so on. Alan's plans had a simple arithmetic which made him a tycoon in a matter of months. With the best will in the world, I couldn't see it happening.

Steve T. in Hackney was going to open his own record shop. He owed rent arrears of nearly £900, an old credit-card bill of £500 and a less formal but considerably more dangerous local debt of £400. Jamie and his girlfriend from Graham Road were going to start a band with their own record label. Their time-table for success was rigorous. They were counting on platinum sales in the first year. Both were unemployed, living in one bed-sit, sharing bathroom and kitchen. Jamie's girlfriend was five months pregnant. 'Anwar', the francophile Sikh from Islington, had learnt something valuable from his fourteen months of living with his large family in a Tower Hamlets bed and breakfast hotel: he had concluded that the true path to riches lay in running a hotel housing homeless families paid for by the

DSS. He asked me to let him know if I saw any good available properties on my travels.

In Botolph's the dreams were even more outrageous. One young man was going to be a television star with his own series – a nude game show on late-night television. A bronchitic twenty-eight-year-old man firmly believed that he would be playing first division football before the year was out. A man with the unlikely name of Randolph showed me sheets of closely scribbled costing schemes for the church renovation business he was proposing. He invited me to invest. A suntanned Glaswegian whispered to me that in a couple of weeks he would be flying to Antigua to open a bar with starter capital provided by his extensive underworld associates.

It's easy to list these fantasies. It's cruel too. They're embarrassing. It was devastating to hear such elaborate schemes coming from such wrecked people. Embarrassing – but also curiously dignified. God knows, I have enough megalomaniac dreams of my future self. Nobel Prize winner, first Irish Test cricketer, orator, genius and general sex god. In the end, the dreams these people nurtured were as admirable as any others. Their imaginations refused to be crushed by acceptance of their allotted victim status. In their dreams, as in all our dreams, they refused the role of victim. They acted successfully, spectacularly, prosperously. I had to acknowledge the personal substance in these private dynamisms.

But these dreams remained haggard and cramped by their corrosive lives. Their greater fatalism thrived at their wrong end of plutocratic Britain. In this frame of mind, the mumblings of professional politicians take on a new and galling comedy. In a month when MPs voted themselves an unprecedented pay rise and a clutch of Whitehall mandarins commanded some stunning income boosts, I sat with Anwar on his ragged sofa in Tower Hamlets. He said, 'The politicians don't care. I don't see them here. They're doing OK, why should they worry about Anwar? I'm a poor Paki. I'm only one vote and I'm not the vote they need.'

Often I struggled to deal with the passivity and pessimism I encountered. Half of the time I tried to hold firm to some idea of possibility, of improvability. Otherwise, I concurred with lowered eyes or mumbled knowing adages of despair. If I wasn't a fatalist, I was a fool. If I wasn't a fool, I was a fatalist. With that attitude, you can't really win. Or, as someone corrected me, with that attitude, you're not *supposed* to win.

The jobless, the ignored, the deprived are eviscerated by pessimism. It is a response that the architects and advocates of 'political realism' must surely commend. Such fatalism dissipates the possibility of effective protest or self-determination. This is not an accident. At this end of the market, if you step on people hard enough, if you catastrophically reduce their potential and opportunity, they stay stepped on. Unity or struggle are impossible for a community whose energies must be so entirely devoted to daily survival. It's simple but it's brilliant.

Parts of London are drowning. The waters are closing in on Hackney. Poll tax, the Child Benefit freeze, the loathed Social Fund, council rent rises, administrative cuts in the DSS, thwarted local authority housing schemes: these are all new factors in a degrading equation. They are adding new multiples to what was already considered an insoluble problem.

London poverty is tough. The city's grey-blue blur fails to illuminate the lives of its poorest. London's prosperous pockets are a constant goad for London's poor. London can seem to live only for those with money: to those folk London doffs its cap. The inane, flickering warmth of the genial, generous city doesn't seem to make it far out of Chelsea. London poverty is tough. Its complex dramas are played out in bed-sits, teeming flats and crumbling tenements, streets, hovels and poky holes of every kind. Grimy walls and pestilential floors press in and advance upon the exponent of poverty. He breathes room-stale air all the years of his life. In his cupboard, in his council kennel, he has no space, he has no freedom, he has no money. He has nothing but the prospect of worse.

GLASGOW

GLASGOW

I spent three days in Glasgow.

Towards the end of my time in London, this book was fast becoming a failure or, at best, a book about failure. The failure was mine. I was failing and *had* failed to cope. What I had seen and heard in London was more than I could endure. Before I set out, I had fancied myself resolute, confident and competent. It was fancy. I had nothing near the emotional and moral resources necessary to bear true witness to the suffering and hardship I had encountered. Constant exposure to a multiplicity of dreadful situations and stories defeated me.

I had wanted to avoid academic or journalistic objectivity or dispassion and this was the result – half a book and half a writer. There were moments in London when I felt that I had entered hell. In truth, I didn't have far to go. Hell was next door, a stone's throw away. I wondered how I had avoided it for so long.

Glasgow was beyond me. Cities take time to yield the colour of their heart and blood and bones. The marrow of a city becomes only ponderously apparent as you grow comfortable with the place. Glasgow daunted me. Though obviously much smaller than London, it had seemed unmanageably vast – much bigger and much scarier than London. It sounds like the worst of futile paradoxes, but I think that this is because London is an aggregate of different cities. Bethnal Green or Barnet or Hackney or Highgate share few characteristics apart from gen-

eral latitude. These city units are separate, sometimes even con-
flicting. That's not to say that Glasgow was homogeneous but
it was certainly consistent in its nature. There were too many
places in Glasgow where I could see too much of the rest of the
city. In Hackney or Whitechapel all I could see was Hackney
or Whitechapel, I could feel secure in the borders of Tower
Hamlets or Bethnal Green and happy with their size. In the
tight, jostling streets of Hackney what I was writing felt relevant, almost visceral. In Glasgow, I saw wide prospects and
massive urban vistas which intimidated me and made what I
was doing seem puny and risible.

Anyway, even without any of that, I wouldn't have stayed
in Glasgow. London had done me in. I'd been harried, harrowed
and miserable there. I'd been lied to, threatened and mucked
about. Some guy had pulled a knife on me in Hackney one
night (It had been an almost polite exchange – speculative,
dilettante). Gabrielle's husband would probably dog my every
future step with his extreme pugilistic intentions.

I flew back to Belfast and did a Hally. I snuggled under the
bedclothes. After a couple of days I called Donovan at his hotel
in Glasgow. I told him that I wasn't going back to Glasgow.
Donovan was hopping mad, naturally. He fumed and raged
while I set the telephone on the desk and smoked a couple of
cigarettes. When I picked it up again, he had calmed somewhat.
He was now using the 'I'm very disappointed in you' gambit.
I asked him if he was still keeping his diary. He said that he
was. I asked him if he recalled how impressed I had been by it.
Yes, he recalled that. I asked him if he remembered boasting
that, if given the chance, he was sure that he could write better
than me. Uneasily, he replied that he did, vaguely.

I told him to write Glasgow himself.

DONOVAN IN GLASGOW

SUNDAY 26 AUGUST

I'm writing this on the train to Glasgow. Three hours of the journey left. Robert saw me off at Euston. He looked terrible and talked despairingly over bad coffee and stale pastries. Robert didn't want me to go. I think after all the grief he's had in London he's dreading moving on to Glasgow.

The train is very full and I couldn't find a smoking carriage so I'm not having a great journey. I've been studying some Walker Evans photographs. The thought of trying to photograph another city bothers me. I know very little about Glasgow. It seems an absurd way to arrive at a new place. 'Excuse me, Constable, could you direct me to some visually impressive slums?' I think I'm becoming obsessive. Every time I chat casually to someone on a bus or in a queue, I find myself probing for slum knowledge. So far, people haven't taken to this approach at all. Robert's always talking about having the courage to be wrong, about the integrity of the mistake. Well, I'm doing him proud here.

I go through the images that I think I've captured in London. I find that I'm not sure if I'm getting close to the truth. I've been constantly trying to avoid making people look like victims, but I'm still confused. Photographing deprived people is difficult because one way or another I'm using them to make pictures.

SAME EVENING

Got to Glasgow without a cigarette. Finding somewhere to stay was awful. I walked through streets completely unknown to me until I finally found a b. & b. It's £12 a night and has a park opposite. Compared to some of the places we used in London, it's paradise. It's quite a smart area and very similar to the posher bits of Belfast. Feel relatively at home.

I went to a bar on the corner and made some conversation with the barman. Eventually, I felt comfortable enough to ask him about deprived areas in Glasgow. He said that they didn't really exist and that I should be honoured to be in the Cultural Capital of Europe. I didn't like this kind of taxi-driver bullshit so I sat down and finished my drink alone. For all I know, Glasgow might be just wonderful, all nice and prosperous. Robert had told me to go to Blackhill. He advised me not to be fooled by immediate impressions of this city, by its city centre or suburban bullishness. He said that the poor areas formed satellites around the city.

Still depressed though. Almost on the point of getting the train back to London. Didn't obviously. Sit now on b. & b. bed, watching football and thinking about tomorrow.

MONDAY 27 AUGUST

Today was one of those days when you shoot anything that looks interesting. I photographed non stop – perhaps a hundred exposures – probably looking all the same. I was aware of this at the time but it never makes any difference. I just felt compelled to do it. It seemed the only way to start in a place of which I'm so ignorant. I will do anything to find the subject.

The day began with me walking from Argyle Street in Yorkhill to the city outskirts. 8.00 a.m. when I set off. School kids everywhere, factory doors opening for the week, women and men walking in the slightly different way of all slightly different cities. The bakeries and all the tiny shops opened. I visited all of them, talked to everyone. I spent over an hour in a launderette waiting for just the right customer. She/he/it didn't arrive, naturally. Continued walking. Shutter finger itching. Looking for nothing in particular and got nothing in particular. Then suddenly after four hours of walking (Robert always found my treks hilarious) I found that I'd shot ten reels. All crap probably. Desperation was setting in. Glasgow is very dusty and spare and wide. It's beautiful sometimes in certain attitudes but it doesn't have Belfast's mountains. I began sneaking into people's back gardens to scout around for items of interest. Nothing to do with the book but I was finally having a good time. I came upon the railroad and decided to follow it simply because I remember looking out as the train pulled into the city yesterday. No joy. About five o'clock I started to walk back but I was completely fucked so I got the train. I had totally failed on a day that had buzzed with activity and beautiful light. The train stopped due to a points failure. Everybody got off and waited for another. A small boy offered to sell me a colour photograph of a Scottish footballer for £2. When I refused he offered to tell me a joke for 50p. I paid him. The joke was bad and very filthy. I complained but didn't get a refund. I was about to take his photograph when he said that it would cost me a fiver. I asked him to go away. He told me he would for £1. I was so tired I gave it to him.

Another train came and we boarded. A stout man smoking a tiny fag-end approached me. He was short, wore a green jumper, canvas trousers and scuffed Doc Martens shoes. We talked about the joke-selling boy for a while. Politely as possible, I asked him where the real shitholes in Glasgow were. Obviously too polite. He took me for a tourist and started pointing out the cathedrals and museums. I interrupted and told him the full truth. I was from Belfast (I'd already found that this went down well here) and was in Glasgow making a book with a friend about poverty. He almost grabbed me and pulled me off the train at his stop. He was delighted to help me and told me numerous childhood stories about the bad old good old days in areas such as Blackhill and the Circuit. His name was Bill but he liked to be called Fish. I called him Fish.

Fish had a security business which he said was doing well. I liked him. Very upfront and pretty funny. We went to a social club for a drink. Talked, played pool and had a pretty good time. He told me that he could name at least twenty friends who had been hospitalized at some time or another for malnutrition-related diseases. He was pretty passionate about it. Like many others in the club (all men) Fish was divorced and remarried. He lived on an estate near an old steel works which was now totally gone. His father had worked there once. He was philosophical about industrial decay.

Fish and I walked into an area called the Circuit. Circular it was indeed and fucking dreadful. Houses were totally dilapidated, no shops as such. As far as photography went I had found a subject. I spent a feverish hour photographing until the light fell away and I was forced to stop. Again, it reminded me greatly of Belfast. The decay. The wilful council neglect – even the graffiti – UVF and IRA were plastered on every available wall, a little touch of home. The houses were generally block-like structures built in the Sixties and a real nightmare. Only half of the estate was still inhabited. Fish had lived here during his first marriage. No one hassled us and there seemed to be very little hostility and danger for such a rough area – again, like Belfast and unlike London. There were no squats which surprised me considering that so many buildings were empty. I remember particularly one image – a clothes-line with a series of bricked-up windows and doors behind it. It was a desolate sight hinting at all kinds of need and loss. Photographing it seemed a pathetic response to what it told me.

Such sights satisfied me. They were what I was looking for. I realized that Glasgow was as bad as, if not worse than, London in terms of deprivation and want. It was very different but just as deprived. London seemed corrupt where Glasgow seemed only redundant and of course I knew Belfast was both. Bill took me back to the social club and we got drunk.

TUESDAY 28 AUGUST

This morning I woke up with a note saying 'Go to Blackhill and ask for Pat. Get number 4 bus under bridge at Central St.' Very excited about this piece of paper but couldn't quite remember how it had got there. Probably Fish looking after me again. Useless though – today Glasgow is dark as night. Punishment for my boozing last night. My light-meter barely reads and to take a shot I'd probably need 800 ASA film with a shutter of 125 – 'summer.' I'd like to see anybody try that little stunt with a hangover like this one.

Anyway, it's not so bad. I'm pretty weary and need a little break. I had breakfast in the basement here. Posters of Sydney Bridge, Rome, Hong Kong, etc., all surrounded by crappy tables with terrible food. Interesting. Equally interesting were the customers. I'm glad to see that I'm not the strangest looking patron here. There was a middle-aged hippie woman who came in in her bare feet, arm in arm with her husband and both of them wearing 'Glasgow: Cultural Capital' T-shirts. The husband was also barefoot. I felt pretty square in my DMs. Anyway, this couple actually fed each other across the table – like very independent babies.

The rest of the day pretty quiet. No camera work. Rain coming down in sheets. Slept in the afternoon. Rang Robert. He waffled on about language and perception for a while and then told me that he'd been seeing Gabrielle again and that there was some real grief with her husband. He sounded pissed off as usual. Don't know why I bother. He only depresses me.

Watched TV. Felt lonely. Went to bed. Hoped for a weather change.

WEDNESDAY 29 AUGUST

Weather good in the morning. After breakfast I ventured into Blackhill. I was nervous but it was a pleasant walk to the famous bus stop under the bridge. The city was busy and foreign. I knew I was at the right bus stop by looking at the other people queuing. Pensioners and the obviously unemployed. (Robert has a big gripe about the word unemployed. He prefers jobless. He says that people without jobs are employed. They employ themselves in lots of ways. 'Unemployed' is an insult according to Robert.)

Anyway, the bus fare was 60p. Later, many of the people I spoke to from the outlying estates complained about these high bus fares. Their homes were so remote from the city centre that they had to use the buses often. It seemed to be a strain on their budget. A bus came and as people got on I was surprised to see them all dropping the precise fare through a metal slit and once the driver was satisfied with the amount dropped he would let the coins slip into a metal box at the bottom. You had to have the exact money or you didn't get a ride. Totally new to me and the driver gave me a whole lot of lip and wouldn't let me on. I had to get some change and wait half an hour for the next bus. Glaswegian charm is pretty obscure, if you ask me.

On the way to Blackhill, I began thinking about the mysterious Pat that Fish had advised me to see. It was like a clandestine meeting. If I found him I'd be all right. If not, I'd look stupid and would have to shoot an awful lot of exteriors. The bus began to climb and I could see gasworks, high rise flats and an enormous slit in the ground which I later learnt was to be a new motorway. It wasn't pretty.

I got off the bus at a bar near Provanill. Very Sixties. I walked off feeling stupid with my camera strung round my neck. This looked a very rough place, as bad as the best of Belfast. A group of men standing outside some kind of club starting shouting insults at me. They looked interesting and worth photographing. From past experience I knew that, surprisingly, the best way to deal with hassle in the street was to go over and bother them a whole lot. So, I approached them and asked them if they knew someone called Pat who knew someone called Fish. I soon realized that I was dealing with the heart and management of Blackhill. These were the top boys. One of the men stepped forward and said (no enthusiasm), 'Yeah, I'm Pat.'

I explained who I was and what I was doing and, of course, that I was a Belfast boy. I told him about Fish taking me round the Circuit and getting hammered the night before. Thankfully, I was welcomed and all fifteen of us stood outside the club and talked. They made me laugh until my stomach ached and I found myself feeling pretty natural.

Eventually, Pat and I broke off from the group. We arranged to meet everybody in the bookie's which was close to the club outside which we were standing. The bookie's was near yet another social club. Pat then took me to every corner of Blackhill. He ran me ragged.

The Circuit

Saloon, Provanmill

Going to school, Blackhill

Post office, Haghill

Look around, Yorkhill

THE DISPOSSESSED

Jobless men, Blackhill

Bookie's, Blackhill

Overleaf: *Bins, Blackhill*

Pat's daughter, Blackhill

Pat and Mo, Blackhill

Youths, Blackhill

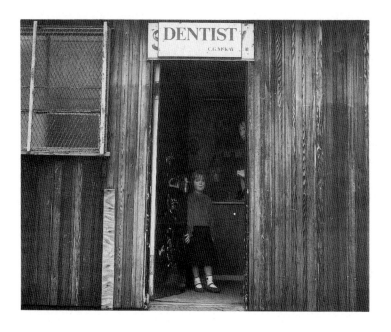

Dentist, Easterhouse

Family, Govan

Single man, Yorkhill

Single woman, Easterhouse

Non-occupancy, The Circuit

'Life has meaning', Haghill

Maisonettes, Easterhouse

Landscape, from Blackhill

Street scene, Central Glasgow

Schoolgirl, Yorkhill

'Be smart', Central Glasgow

Two girls, Blackhill

Woman, Govan

Waiting, Easterhouse

Saturday afternoon, Easterhouse

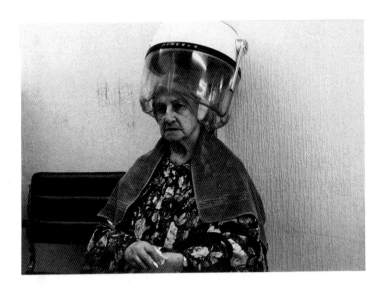

Pensioner, Central Glasgow

Weary man, Central Glasgow

Cut-price shop, Yorkhill

Steve, Haghill

As we talked I began to form an immediate liking for him. He was funny and friendly. He was the only person I had met so far on my travels who did not complain about his conditions and lifestyle. Pat had married young, divorced, remarried. One child, Catherine and a dog. The dog was called Mo, after Mo Johnson, the footballer. The nationalism in Blackhill is as strong as on the Falls, New Lodge, Ballymurphy or any other Belfast area. Pat was fairly hot on that. I actually felt at home. I knew this stuff. Pat reassured me that I would come to no harm. However, he said that if I had been English that would have been a different matter.

The homes in Blackhill formed long strips along deserted roads. Most of the houses were bricked up. To be honest, the whole place already looked like a photograph. At one point I noticed a new Ford Granada looking out of place outside one of the homes. I asked Pat about this and he told me that an eviction was about to take place. I waited around. I'd never seen an eviction before and felt it would make a valuable picture. Anyway, everything was quiet. It transpired that these guys were detectives and they were on a drugs raid. Pat and I were told to get out of the street.

I began photographing. Blackhill is beautiful and ugly. Robert says the same thing about the ghetto where he was born. It can be true. I felt incredibly happy as I worked. It was going well. In London, I had found that I could not photograph the truth without seeing it first and then working with the victims of it. Here the truth was so apparent that it was happening fast and people were so open and quick to friendship. Fish and Pat had almost adopted me already.

I shot for nearly an hour while Pat proved his patience and waited for me. He chatted and laughed. Pat didn't really feel any bitterness towards anyone. Government didn't bother him. He didn't seem to have much interest in what was happening elsewhere. He had lived in Blackhill since he was a child and was destined to remain there or to be moved to an even worse area. As he saw it, whatever happened in the newspapers, no one was going to do him any favours. I liked Pat a lot.

Afterwards he took me back to his house. Over the past few months I'd built up a talent for spotting whether or not people were bringing in money from other sources – new colour television, video recorder, satellite dish, etc. Pat's home was not like this. He had a small portable black and white television and a portable radio, pretty clapped out. The wallpaper was coming down and the carpets were worn. We talked and I photographed him in the hall with his dog. We heard shouting from one of the rooms. After I had finished shooting him, Pat disappeared into this room for some time. It was his wife questioning him about me. More shouting. Meanwhile, I photographed Pat's daughter in the kitchen which was in an appalling state. I felt fairly low about photographing the daughter on the sly, like that. The people I meet trust me and because of that I can become a little bit like them. I feel close to them. But then I do something sneaky like shooting Pat's daughter and I realize that it's my subject that I'm becoming closer to. It's difficult. To make this book, I must do such things. But it is still difficult.

The shouting in Pat's bedroom ended and Pat came out and suggested that we move outside. I told him I'd photographed his daughter and that I hoped he didn't mind. He didn't seem to care one way or another. As we left he showed me a signature he had made on one of the walls when they had moved in. It had made the house his, he felt. He explained that his wife was in bed with a fever and that was all I really learnt about her. He seemed very unbothered by our undignified exit and was full of spirit. He suggested that we go back to the bookie's and meet up with the rest of the lads.

We walked up the road and I watched as groups of pretty girls hung about on the pavements. Pat didn't seem very interested. I moved on with him. At the bookie's we made some bets. I hadn't a clue what to bet on and couldn't understand the odds but it was quite good fun. I even got some pictures in there. Today was just a golden day for photographs. Everybody said goodbye as they drifted into the next room which was the bar. Pat stood swearing at them jokingly as they went and a whole round of comic abuse started. I thought Pat was being polite in staying with me. But then I realized that Pat couldn't go into the bar because he was banned from the place.

The two of us headed out and I bought a few cans of beer. Happy with what I'd shot, Pat and I sat talking and drinking for a few hours *until he left to see his wife. I headed back to Argyle Street and had some dinner.*

I phoned Robert and we had a big fight. He told me that he couldn't come back to Glasgow. I was furious. He's spent less than a week here and for most of that time he hid in somebody's house. He said he was too exhausted to come and that we had to get back to Belfast within the week anyway. I screamed at him so much that the landady came out and asked me to keep it down. He demanded that I return to Belfast by next Wednesday. I protested that after almost three months in London that would only give me about ten days in Glasgow and that this was a bit lopsided. He said that he didn't care and that we had to work in Belfast for at least a couple of months. I said that I had been living in Belfast all my life and that I'd been photographing there since I was fourteen. I knew where to go. I knew what to do. Robert said that this was the precise mistake I was making. I had to go back afresh as if I knew nothing. I had to see it again. Freshly.

THURSDAY 30 AUGUST

Another good day. The summer seems endless in Glasgow. I had been heading back out to Blackhill this morning when I got talking to a young man called Ian. Ian told me that he lived in a squat quite close to the city centre. He had been born and brought up in Edinburgh but had moved to Glasgow to live with his girlfriend. He hadn't had a full-time job since 1987. When I met him he was on his way to a city centre hotel to see if he could get a day's casual work in the kitchens. I asked him if I could come along. As we walked, I told Ian what I was doing in Glasgow. Ian had spent a few months in London looking for work. He had stayed at a friend's flat in Rotherhithe for four months and had spent three days a week working as a waiter or a day-labourer on a building site, while for another three days a week he searched for a full-time permanent job. Ian was very bright and intelligent. He told me that his older brother was already an accountant. Ian, who was twenty-three, was a year younger than this brother. When the elder brother reached the age of sixteen, the family decided that, since the father had been made redundant because of industrial injury, they could only afford one son continuing his education. The elder brother had won that vote and Ian had left school at sixteen and got a job as a storeman for £65 per week. He didn't seem bitter about this at all.

When we got to the hotel, the kitchen manager offered us both a day of kitchen work: washing dishes and cleaning floors. We accepted and went to work. I asked the manager if I could take some photographs and he almost threatened to throw me out. I stopped him by letting him keep my camera in his office to ensure that I wouldn't sneak any photographs when he wasn't looking. I don't know what he was so paranoid about since the big kitchen area was pretty spotless, mostly due to the enormous hard work that Ian, myself and the other casual for the day put into keeping it clean.

It was back-breaking work – really very hard and exhausting. At six o'clock, after eight hours of labour with one half-hour break, the manager gave each of us a cheap brown envelope containing £15 in cash. I was pretty stunned by the amount but Ian seemed happy enough with it and I concluded that this must have been the going rate. We limped away pretty exhausted.

Outside, the city had finished its working day and was beginning to get itself ready for its entertainment and leisure. I felt cut off from that kind of good time. I decided to take some photographs of prosperous Glasgow going about its pastimes, the sky was still bright and the streets were slowly filling with yuppies and groups of youths. Ian was glad to sit on a flight of steps while I worked.

Ian had invited me back to meet his girlfriend and after walking for about twenty minutes we got to his squat. His girlfriend was tall, attractive and friendly but what Ian had forgotten to tell me was that they had a baby son. Their flat, a sitting room/kitchen and a small bedroom, was clean but in poor repair. The walls were lined with cracks, plaster was hanging from some parts of the ceiling and there were holes in the floor where the floorboards had rotted away. They both preferred enduring these conditions to remain close to the city centre rather than being shunted out to somewhere like Blackhill.

We had some tuna and pasta with tomatoes and mushrooms. I had bought some wine and the meal was pleasant. Both Ian and I were exhausted after our day's work. I asked him how many days' casual work he did. He told me that he tried to get three days a week but usually only succeeded twice a week. I took some portraits of them. The woman who had some rooms upstairs came down. Her name was Norma. She was jobless, having been sacked a couple of months before from her last job as a hairdresser. Two of the other six staff had also gone – two employees who hadn't worked there long enough to be entitled to redundancy payments or claims of unfair dismissal. We all talked for a while about money and I went back to the hotel. I had photographed little but I'd had my arms bent in work that only the poor will do. My arms didn't appreciate it.

I felt as though I'd seen more of Glasgow. Wandering round the streets of a city can make you feel like a tourist. Even talking to people doesn't necessarily make you feel much more than a casual visitor. But doing a day's labour in any place makes you feel that it belongs to you at least a little.

I'd taken fewer photographs than I might have but, reviewing them in my mind tonight, I feel more confident about what I might have captured or seen. The distraction of the day's kitchen work limited my time so drastically that I had only precious moments of light in which to work. Perhaps this made me see quicker and clearer. I'll know when I print up, I suppose.

I go to bed. I'm glad now that Robert's not here. Let him sleep it off at home. I can see and show more without his narrative anxieties getting in my way.

I didn't keep my diary with the same regularity after that day. I got too busy and too interested. After another night at the hotel, Ian and Jane, his girlfriend, were kind enough to let me stay at their house for the rest of my time in Glasgow. There was a bare room at the top of the house into which Ian and I dragged an old mattress that Norma from upstairs donated. This jobless, squatting threesome were always kind and generous with me. Both Ian and Norma took an interest in the work I was doing and Ian showed me much of the city that I might otherwise have missed or simply ignored.

Amazingly, I discovered that Jane and Ian gave Norma £15 a week with which Norma bought their week's groceries while she was getting her own. It wasn't that Jane and Ian were helpless or incompetent, it was just that Norma was the goddess of food shopping. Fifteen pounds a week doesn't sound as though it would provide a week's sustenance for two adults and a baby. Norma did amazing work with the money. With the addition of £10 a week of her own money, Norma stocked the communal kitchen to bursting. I had never seen a kitchen as well stocked as Norma's.

Norma had all the frugal shopper's skills. She bought all her fruit and vegetables from market stalls after five o'clock when stallholders would cut prices to clear their stocks. She did the same thing at bakeries. She bought two-day-old bread late in its second day, thirty minutes before it would have to be thrown out. She used supermarket coupons and special offers. Before a bank holiday, Norma charged into supermarkets where meat was sold off at half price or less. She'd buy it almost by the hundredweight and freeze it in their decrepit but large freezer. It usually lasted until the next bank holiday. Ian would swipe the odd catering size drum of coffee, tea, rice or pasta from one of the hotels in which he was chronically underpaid.

Since I was staying there, I demanded that I contribute. I gave Norma £10 and asked her, as an exercise, to keep that amount separate so that I could note down what she managed to purchase with it. I came back that evening to the usual sumptuous abundance of the kitchen. On a worktop there was a separate pile of groceries which was what Norma had spent my money on. It included two loaves of wholemeal bread, a lettuce, ten pounds of potatoes, a pound of onions, a pound of tomatoes, half a pound of mushrooms, two whole beetroots, one green pepper, one red pepper, one pound of oranges, one pound of apples, four bananas, half a pound of Cheddar cheese, two pork chops, one pound of liver, a small whole chicken, some fresh plaice, two bulbs of garlic, some wholegrain rice and three pints of semi-skimmed milk. It looked like an awful lot for a tenner.

I'm sure that this kind of frugal abundance wouldn't be possible for everyone. Norma spent a lot of time planning her campaigns. It was also a very individual skill. It was a talent peculiar to Norma and one of which she was rightly very proud. I asked if I could photograph her while she went on one of her expeditions. She didn't seem all that keen and I didn't want to press her.

Ian took me to the west of the city, Govan, Partick and Maryhill. I spent quite a lot of time there. Great photographs lurked on every corner. It was a desperate area and this suited my vampire camera. Parts of the west of Glasgow are as bad as the Circuit or as bad as Ballymurphy in West Belfast. It surprised me to find that quite a few of the residents of West Glasgow were students. The poll tax, grant freezes, the Student Loans scheme and the difficulty of getting Housing Benefit while in full-time education had all conspired to make many of these people penniless. I talked to a lot of these students. They lived in conditions shared by the ordinary poor families who surrounded them. The students told me that as their conditions had deteriorated, they had found their working-class or unemployed neighbours much more tolerant than before. The old accusations of living comfortably off the taxpayer's state no longer applied and people began to recognize that their plight was often as difficult as any.

Many of the local families welcomed me and talked openly with me as well. When I spoke to someone, it was generally only the most fleeting contact – obviously, I could not get to know most people well. Robert had often said that I didn't need to know people well to photograph. He betrayed his ignorance and prejudice there. There *are*, I admit, moments when only the briefest contact can lead to photographs of insight and sympathy but most of the time I have to know people and places at least relatively well before I can do them justice in my work. It would be easy to run around a deprived area and take two days' worth of award-winning, coffee-table photographs but there would be no truth or honour in them. When I take pictures I feel that I have two obligations. One is to the person who looks at my picture. I have to be clear in what I show or tell them. My second duty is to my subject. I'm never really sure which of these duties is paramount or whether they can co-exist in equal importance. I know that when I was in Glasgow, the obligation I felt to the city, to its people and to the delicacy of a subject like poverty outweighed any other consideration. These people gave me their time too readily and openly for me to take any liberties.

People were always more than happy for me to photograph their children. Some parents even coaxed me into doing this. I had to make promises about sending them prints, promises that I could not possibly have kept. Adults were sometimes very wary about having their own photographs taken. Even those who agreed to it never seemed entirely happy about it. A photographer is faced with an ethical difficulty when confronted by a more or less reluctant subject. If he is to take the photograph, he must be sure that his reasons, that his themes are vital enough to allow him to do so in the face of such discomfort. The willingness of so many people to have their children photographed showed the pride they took in their families. It was very touching.

Even photographing general exteriors in that part of the city was a social experience. People would stop me in the street and ask me what I was doing. They could be encouraging or critical in equal measure. One middle-aged woman with a pramful of twins said, 'You don't have any right to photograph people who aren't aware of you. That's not right.' Which was fair enough. I tried to do that as little as possible but sometimes an accidental and momentary grouping of people would occur on some pavement never to be repeated. I owed it to myself to capture accidental moments.

West Glasgow's streets were sunny and dusty, wide and sometimes bare, sometimes cluttered with debris. Men, women and children picked their way through these streets like movie stars. Glaswegians have special faces. They were striking and handsome, each one a photograph. Their city was in their faces. Pat from Blackhill had been a fine example with his good build, his scars and his big smile. His face had been marked by where he lived more than most.

It had been different in London. The people there had their own mark, true, but it was a different one for every area or borough. West Ham/East Ham boys were ratty and fat. Stoutness hit both sexes at all ages. Whitechapel folk were grey and haunted. Hackney people were strung out and thinned down by Hackney's harsh atmosphere. Glasgow people were different. They were firmer, less wobbly or slight.

I began to walk the streets more aimlessly than before. I couldn't learn everything about the people I photographed quickly or casually but I could learn a lot about taking pictures. It didn't matter how long it took. If I was comfortable with what I was doing, taking a picture could be a way of learning, a new way of seeing. My brilliant third day in Glasgow had been like that.

After a few days, when I had exhausted the attractions and usefulness of street-wandering, I took a mad notion to go round door to door. I encountered a lot of elderly pensioner women who thought I was going to rape and rob them and who wouldn't let me in. I suppose telling them that I was making a book could easily have seemed like a lame criminal's excuse.

Predictably, only a few people let me into their homes after this eccentric approach. One of these people, Jack D., opened his door wearing a string vest, a fag-end drooping from one corner of his mouth. His hair was thinning and sandy but his broad, lined face was appealing and friendly. He told me, as he stood on the doorstep, that he worked in one of the Glasgow markets. He sold fish. His hands were rough and scarred from his job but beautiful as only a workman's hands can be.

Jack invited me into his house and made me sit on a creaky sofa in his sitting room. It wasn't much of a room. It was clean but pretty bare and uncomfortable. His wife sat on a rickety chair opposite me. She seemed to be mentally handicapped or mentally ill in some way, though neither Jack nor I openly referred to this. He told me that he had to keep the curtains closed because she was photophobic. She had a strange expression on her face which was a smile, though it looked more like a grimace or a scowl. The effect was surprisingly content, anyway. She clung tightly to Jack when he pulled his armchair close to hers. Jack was a true Working Man – blunt, strong and likeable. His muscles bulged at me in the light of the dim room. His politics were simple. 'It's hard to live if you can't eat. I'll do any kind of work to feed us.' I couldn't argue with this and didn't feel like foisting any of Robert's universal dispossession theories. Sitting there, shirtless, heavy and muscular, Jack impressed me equally with his strength and his obvious tenderness in dealing with his wife.

Newspapers were strewn all over the floor. I was surprised at their messiness in this otherwise tidy home. Jack explained that his wife had an obsession with newspapers. She demanded that they should never be thrown out and Jack was not permitted to tidy them away. It was hard, he said, to keep printmarks and inky smudges off the walls. I noticed that his wife's hands were dark with newsprint. There was only one light in the room. A single bare bulb hanging from the ceiling. Jack said that he would buy a shade for it the next time he had a fiver spare for decoration. I asked him how long he thought it would be until a fiver would be surplus. He told me that on £87 per week for both of them, he suspected that the lampshade would take a time in coming.

We had some coffee in the kitchen while his wife struggled

around with some pots and pans. I took some pictures but I knew that I'd never print them. They would have looked great in a crass way. The distressed wife, the bare rooms, the drawn curtains, the single bare light bulb and Jack in his string vest. However, that cliché wouldn't have been anywhere near the truth of either of them. Some things are too complicated for photographs.

I stopped knocking on strangers' doors. I didn't need to do that to meet people. In Glasgow, people struck up an acquaintance with me at the drop of a hat. There was none of the distrust I had encountered in London. In shops, in buses, trains, pubs or on the streets I could always find plenty of people willing and keen to talk. Sometimes I was desperate that Robert should meet and talk with some of these people but most of the time, to be honest, I was glad that he would not. I could photograph and talk without his interference. I didn't want the people I met to be invaded by Robert's writing. He kept many of the people he met well away from me.

I met old Frank on a street corner. Frank was nearly seventy years old. He talked a lot about the last war and about his failed marriage. He had one son whom he hadn't seen for thirty years. He only talked happily about the war. He was the complete old soldier. He talked about individual battles an hour at a time. He wouldn't talk much about his present circumstances even though he looked like the poorest person I had seen in Glasgow – much more like someone I might have met at Botolph's or Tooley Street Hostel. He told me that he lived in a two-room flat in Easterhouse. He liked me because I was Irish and he claimed to have served in the British Army in South Armagh in 1972, though that would have made Frank the only fifty-five-year-old squaddy in Northern Ireland at the time. Frank's face was dirty and red from heat. He told me that he liked to wander around the city. He kept himself to himself. He didn't want the responsibility of knowing people in a similar situation as himself, that is, people as poor as him. He believed that the unemployed were work shy and that they should be forcibly conscripted into the army. His words trailed away into mumbles every few minutes. He was obviously badly broken. It was also plain that despite what he said about the two-room flat in Easterhouse, he was homeless. He asked me if I could spare him some money until next week. I gave him a fiver.

The streets were sometimes crowded with people or events. In a crumbling cul-de-sac in an estate in West Glasgow, I saw a young man lying injured on the road. A couple of people stood round him uselessly. I went over. He had obviously taken some kind of overdose. I had seen the same thing in London when one of the Botolph's clients had taken an overdose and collapsed in the men's toilets. Then I had been terrified and unsure whether to help the man or photograph him lying there with the blood from his head wound already staining the mops against the wall. Melanie, the Botolph's nurse, had told me to take the photograph now and worry about it later. There was nothing I could do for him that Melanie could not have done since she was a professional nurse and I was a professional voyeur.

This young Glaswegian was a different matter. People were walking past him as he lay there. I asked one of the people bending over him whether anyone had called an ambulance. He didn't know so I told him to go and do it himself to make sure. I crouched over the unconscious youth and checked whether he was still breathing. He was, thankfully. He had needle marks everywhere I looked. His arms were nearly black from needle abuse and his arteries were thick and knotted as though his veins had turned to rubber. There were even (and this really bothered me) puncture marks between his fingers. It shook me badly. I waited for the ambulance to come. By the time he had been taken away, I was out of it. Scared and sick.

Those were some of the photographs that I *didn't* take. But they weren't missed opportunities. The things I learnt from people like Ian and Norma or Jack D. informed and improved the photographs that I went on to take of other people or events.

They showed me something of Glasgow and once I was able to see it, I could photograph it.

In particular, meeting people like that showed me how I should photograph the buildings and landscapes of Glasgow. I took one photograph near Blackhill which I felt would be a good example of what I felt or thought about the city. The photograph is of a gas-holder in the foreground beside some wasteland. In the distance on the right-hand side is a nest of seven enormous tower blocks. The landscape was desolate but also weirdly beautiful. It showed two generations of Glaswegian architecture – the gasworks, which were beautiful and closed down, and the towers, which were ugly and should have been closed down. It reminded me of America. It was a dangerous, forbidding area where the community was dominated by its architecture. A new road was being built on the waste ground. It was some kind of city or motorway link. It seemed to be breaking through this area and on towards the city. This road would not have been built in a middle-class suburb. It was a road ignoring the area in which it was built. It further ignored and marginalized the area.

I liked taking this photograph because I wasn't sure that I understood the picture entirely. I certainly didn't understand the area. The buildings and roads of this place seem to have been built and were being built without reference to the people of the area. The city seemed to be growing without them or against them.

There was another moment which excited me so much that I decided that I would include the print in the book no matter how badly it turned out. It was in Yorkhill, near the hotel where I had first stayed. It wasn't a particularly deprived area but it had its run-down streets and parts. I was photographing a street when I glanced round and saw a young schoolboy standing outside a cheap grocer's shop, waiting to cross the road. I wheeled round fast and took the shot before he could set off across the road. I feared that the focus might be poor but I didn't care. The moment was perfect. The shop was tiny and shabby, there was a collection of cheap goods outside – baked beans, soup cans, cat litter, cheap toilet rolls and a few old vegetables in a scuffed plastic basket. This place was less than budget shopping. It was a last resort. I had captured the moment when this healthy-looking, vigorous schoolboy had paused in front of the kind of diet and household goods that had produced him. Yet he was so healthy in the grime of the street.

I liked this shot because it was a small happening. It was a tiny non-event with a meaning that was slow to reveal itself; as with all small happenings. A 'No Poll Tax' poster which some-one had tried to tear away, the crappy food, the schoolboy. Robert told me that twentieth-century fiction had discovered the epic in the mundane. Photographers have been doing that for a hundred and fifty years.

Poverty in Glasgow seemed very different from the poverty I had seen in London. There wasn't the same strangeness in Glasgow. Robert said that this was because it's easy to forget that London is a capital city and that first cities have characteristics and pitfalls that apply to all their citizens and visitors. I think there was another difference. Poor Glaswegians seemed less destroyed by poverty. Proportionally more of them were poor, it seemed, and perhaps that made the experience easier to bear because it was so widely shared. Glasgow is not like London. It is not a city divided between poverty and wealth. Of course, Glasgow has middle-class, prosperous areas but the city has nothing to match the wealthier parts of London. Glaswegians are not goaded by a sense of local comparison and injustice the way that people in Hackney are.

But the thing that surprised me most in Glasgow was the same thing that had surprised me most in London. I had set out to take photographs about poverty and, to be frank, I had expected that I would be taking photographs of a type of unhappiness. I thought that misery would be common among deprived people. There *was* much unhappiness among the people I met. People suffered and grieved under many different stresses. But I was surprised by how much contentment or happiness people managed for themselves under such dreadful conditions. That they could prevail at all in such circumstances was admirable. That they could actually make liveable lives out of their predicament was extraordinary.

I encountered many memorable people and places in Glasgow. I photographed some of them. People and places reacting to and enduring their deprivation as best they could. Jim from Haghill, who sold second-hand furniture and bought me more drinks than he could afford or I could drink. Jim talked about his seven children: 'I'm glad it wasn't eight.' He was obsessed with his family with whom he lived in a two-bedroomed house with a leaking roof. 'I don't want my children to leave the house until they get married,' he said. 'I don't want them leaving and getting into trouble or drugs, or the girls getting pregnant. I want them to have somewhere to go when they leave and someone to go with.' He talked for hours about his favourite cars and about Stirling Moss, his favourite racing driver. According to Jim: 'Life's hard but that doesn't make it bad.'

A darker memory of a middle-aged woman holding onto a lamp-post on a street in Easterhouse. When I asked her if she was all right, she shouted 'Get Charlie, please bring him back!' I was frightened. I imagined that Charlie might be a deceased husband or son. I asked her where she lived. She tried to point but she nearly fell over when she took her arm from the lamp-post. The woman was sobbing now and there was no one around. I felt helpless. I ran to the nearest house and rang the doorbell. A woman with her hair in curlers answered the door. I told her what was happening. 'She'll have to work it out for herself,' the woman said and disappeared. I went back to the woman who was still holding onto the lamp-post. 'Get me Charlie!' she screamed.

But most of all, I remember the end of a bad day in Haghill. Walking away from the estate, I met a man called Steve who kept pigeons. He took me to a twelve-foot tower of corrugated iron half-way up a scrubby slope on the edge of the estate. 'This is where we let them go,' he said. He gave me a demonstration. We climbed into the tower and he put one of his birds in my hands. He told me that on the other side of the estate, half a mile away, his friend was waiting in a similar tower. He told me to let the bird go and it would fly to his friend in the other tower. I let the bird go. My companion watched the beauty of the bird in flight. 'People laugh at pigeons but they're beautiful fliers,' he said. After a few minutes the bird flew back to us, released by the man in the other tower. 'Hold out your arms,' said Steve. I held out my arms and the pigeon landed gently on my elbow. I photographed Steve until it grew dark and we could no longer see the birds and could only hear the whipping of their wings as they flew and landed.

BELFAST

ONE

Moira from Clonard. Thirty-three, two children, no husband, no parents, no money. Moira had spent three years working the city centre streets, giving relief at knockdown prices. She had given it up. Prostitution in Belfast is a very different creature from prostitution in London or Manchester or Bristol or Glasgow. In Belfast, particularly in Catholic West Belfast, the whore's lot is not a happy one.

Moira said that she'd been hospitalized twice, paid visits to casualty beyond number and had often just patched herself up with Band-Aid or cotton wool and Scotchtape. She had finally rejected prostitution when a man pulled a knife on her.

Moira now worked behind the bar in a local social club. Coercion, threats, subdued, potential violence were the good nights. The bad nights were brawls and kneecappings in the toilets. Moira received less than £2 per hour for this work. It was bad, she admitted, but it was a fair way better than having some fat mad bastard leaving his knife between her ribs.

Moira's home wasn't very nice. It was clean enough (you'll struggle to find a truly dirty home in East or West Belfast – they're funny that way), but that was the best you could say. Moira slept on a mattress with only a woollen blanket for bedding. As always the children fared well – decent cots, good clothes, multitudes of clapped-out but serviceable toys. Furniture was largely a pipe dream here and carpets were some way off.

Social workers camped outside; there were special coffee cups for the vice squad regulars. Priests lurked in the garden ready for infamy. I gathered that a couple of men on the street, ex-boyfriends, would come round and knock Moira about a bit just in case. DSS geostationary satellites winked overhead, clocking her movements.

It's dull, isn't it?

That's the thing about outrage, about injustice or calamity. It can be tedious beyond words. Stereotypes, stock responses, attention-spans tangle themselves into a daunting jumble of alien consequence and cause. Even Moira was pretty bored by it.

Moira had attended St Dominic's, an excellent girls' grammar school on the Falls Road. She had eleven O levels, six of them Bs and above. That's a whole lot of O levels for a poverty-stricken, unmarried, ex-prostitute mother. Things had happened, she said. I'd learnt already that when women said 'things' they meant men happened. Men had obviously happened to Moira in a very big way. Of all the people I had met, Moira seemed the one whose situation was the most worthy of despair. Moira was well fucked into the next century. She had about half an hour before some evangelical arm of the caring state robbed her of her children. Her handful of excellence certificates wasn't going to cut much ice in the Clonard employment market. She would be caught defrauding the DSS in her tiny necessary way and the second volume of her criminal record would open.

Moira dreamt of the then Prime Minister often. She loathed Margaret Thatcher with a pale, sickly resolve. When she discovered that I had been at Cambridge, she asked me what the deal was with those people. I waffled grandly. She told me that for her, Margaret Thatcher was proof that there was a God. It wasn't goodness that convinced Moira. It was wickedness. There simply had to be some kind of final retribution. Even mathematically, it was outrageous to suppose that they could get away with it. It was asymmetrical, it did not compute.

Moira's clutch of O levels did not equip her to make any sensible estimation of her future. Her coming days and years were flat and colourless with the certainty of poverty and failure. It took only a small part of Moira's considerable wit to realize that there was little prospect of an improvement in her circumstances. She referred openly to this hopelessness and it discomfited me somewhat. I mean, what *do* you say to someone when they tell you that they can see only despair ahead? You can't exhort them to buck up a bit.

Moira said that she was not sure of how she had got into such a position – it was an aggregate of unfortunate incidents and difficult outcomes. She was ignorant of where exactly her life would go on to take her. What pained her most was the probability of her children being removed into care. She knew that this was coming and she knew that it would come soon but she had no plans for coping with it comfortably. Her children were guiltless and were, as she saw, already being punished well enough.

I didn't see much of Moira. Nobody really saw much of Moira, apart from her children. She seemed to move around cloaked by some kind of invisibility as if her predicament was simply too much for others to bother themselves with. Moira's plight *was* something of a conversation stopper. I couldn't figure out whether Moira's solitude was voluntary or merely endured. Whichever, it seemed pretty total. Moira managed her bi-weekly crises all by herself.

Her situation was close to collapse. I suspected that the prosperous half of her street were running a book on her chances of seeing out the winter. The odds would have been long indeed. Moira knew this well enough but still she struggled against her inevitable dispossession.

'I know it's only a matter of time,' she said, 'but I've still got to pretend that it isn't going to happen. I tell myself that the kids are still going to be with me next year. I'd fall apart now if I admitted to myself how bad things are for me. If I try to go on – you never know what might happen in the end.'

Moira knew exactly what was going to happen – everything she didn't want to happen would happen in abundance. Again, it seemed to me that fantasy had become the refuge of those I was encountering, those whose conditions and prospects had become more than they could contemplate. Moira's fantasy of keeping her children was a noble one, a dream that should have been realizable but, sadly, it was fantastic.

TWO

For a provincial capital in an under-populated country, Belfast is very famous indeed. It is famous for the violent political conflict of the last twenty-odd years. Little else is famous about Belfast. It has bred no famous painters; no great novels are set in Belfast. It has no great orchestra, its university is not celebrated. The 'troubles' have made Belfast a celebrity.

Few people who do not live in Northern Ireland know much about Belfast apart from its roster of political deaths and maimings. Few people realize how beautiful Belfast can be – a low-lying city at the mouth of a great bay ringed and nudged by mountains. Few people have heard of the city's dynamism and warmth. Few imagine the emotional substance necessary for a city to survive traumas like those Belfast has survived. Few are aware of the extent and prevalence of social deprivation in this televised town.

Northern Ireland has the highest unemployment rate in the United Kingdom (14.4 per cent in January 1990). Fifty-three per cent of the province's unemployed are long-term unemployed. Gross earnings in Northern Ireland are the lowest *per capita* in the United Kingdom. Expenditure on most state cash benefits is higher per head in Northern Ireland than for the United Kingdom as a whole. Expenditure on Supplementary Benefits, Child Benefit, sickness and invalidity benefits is notably higher than the United Kingdom average. Households in the province are least likely to have most consumer durable goods compared with other parts of the United Kingdom. In all the areas it is bad to do badly, Belfast is doing badly.

A common tactic to explain or illuminate Belfast's present violence is to refer to Belfast's violent past. Historical reference seems to indicate inevitable outcomes and trends. Perhaps such a tactic might be applied to Belfast's economic conditions as well. Would we find that Belfast's widespread deprivation was historically inevitable?

The history of Belfast is one of conquest and conflict. Up until the late sixteenth century Belfast had consisted of the usual clump of lean-tos, middens and shacks. In 1571 an English attempt at conquest under Sir Thomas Smith had failed. Elizabeth I then sent the Earl of Essex who also failed. In the end, Arthur Chichester conquered the recalcitrant province. His methods were traditionally brutal and effective. Chichester was the true founder of Belfast.

In 1605 the Plantation began. In a huge effort of social engineering, Scottish landowners came to Ulster where they commandeered vast swathes of land owned by native clans. Chichester decided to make Belfast the model plantation town in this model example of plantation.

In 1613, the town was granted a charter of incorporation, ensuring a borough with guaranteed Protestant representatives. For the next fifty years, the Ulster syndrome showed its paces, the eternal problem of the Irish, and the province was near to ungovernable. There was fighting and killing between the local communities, old and new – back and forth between the native Catholic Irish, the Scottish Protestants, the Royalists and the Parliamentarians.

Then Oliver Cromwell arrived to quieten things down. Cromwell's technique – decapitate first and don't bother asking questions at all – did the job in short order and left a lasting mark on the temperature of Ulster's political schisms. After painting the town his particular red in Drogheda, Cromwell reconquered Belfast in four days.

The arrival of Cromwell's army boosted Belfast's economy.

It quickly became an important port, sending Ulster's considerable agricultural surplus abroad to Britain, France, Spain and even to the new American colonies. In 1660, Belfast occupied eighty-six acres and its population was only one thousand strong. The town traded corn, butter and beef. There were cornmills, a sugar refinery and an embryonic iron industry.

A new chapter of grief opened when William of Orange (King Billy, modern Protestant icon and all-round general good guy – blessed by the Pope, incidentally), arrived on the scene. James II took Belfast, but Belfast didn't take to him. William and James fought it out in Ulster – the old to and fro – the Battle of the Boyne, the siege of Derry. James II was out of Belfast in five months. Gratefully, William passed a set of penal laws depriving Catholics of the right to vote, to buy land or enter the professions.

Despite the various turmoils, Belfast's population grew steadily. Only 8500 in 1757, it had risen to 20,000 by 1800. The bourgeoisie had become prominent. Belfast's merchants set up their own linen halls. Local brickworks increased their production to supply the materials with which the town was being built. More than 13,000 people worked in Belfast's cotton industry.

After the American War of Independence and the subsequent tumult, Belfast stuck fast to its allegiance to the Crown. However, international republicanism led to a radicalism among the Protestant intelligentsia of the town. When Britain went to war with Republican France, the Protestant dissenters of Belfast were seen as traitors and rebels. A reactionary militia occupied the town, expecting a French-backed invasion under the command of the radical, Wolfe Tone. It never came. The radicals were arrested and executed.

Between 1801 and 1841, the population of Belfast increased from 20,000 to around 70,000. A third of the population were Catholics from the countryside, driven to the city by rural hardship. Investment surged and trade boomed. The massive labour surplus, low wage expectations and lack of tariffs boosted the economy further. Housing, schools and public buildings sprouted up all over the town. The harbour was improved and the railways came in 1839. Town planning was precise and competent to deal with rising population and economic growth.

For the next thirty years, Belfast was a boom town without parallel. The population exploded from 70,000 to 174,000 by 1871. The rural economy had collapsed and the town was flooded with new citizens. Banks were founded, the harbour was improved further and Belfast pushed itself to the forefront of contemporary industrial and technological sophistication.

Belfast officially became a city in 1888 and by 1901 the population had doubled again to 349,000. The city's rate of growth at that time was greater than that of any other city in Britain. It became a shipbuilding and engineering paragon. Unaided by patronage or advantage, it built itself.

The growing Catholic population increased the sectarian tension. Housebuilding quadrupled and the city began to order itself into Protestant or Catholic enclaves. But corporate and municipal confidence was high. Many of Belfast's public buildings date from this period and demonstrate well the prevalent mood of economic certainty.

The twentieth century began with Belfast buoyant. The city was the world's foundry, building more ships than anywhere else on the planet. Belfast firms manufactured for massive export markets. Its customs revenue was second only to London and Liverpool. Belfast led the world in shipbuilding, ropeworks, linen spinning, tobacco factories, dry docks and much else. Belfast was a mighty economic giant.

The First World War was the beginning of the end. The Easter Rising in Dublin in 1916 was a violent assertion of Irish aspirations to Home Rule. Coming as it did in the midst of Britain's conflict with Germany, it set Belfast Protestants irrevocably against Home Rule. Though Ulster Catholics as well as Ulster Protestants had been slaughtered in their thousands fighting in the First World War, Loyalists claimed that the Catholic minority had not done their bit. The troubles that followed the Easter Rising in the South now spread to Ulster. Protestant gangs indulged in acts of violence against the Catholic minority during the bitter summer of 1919. A pattern of fear and retribution began to establish itself indelibly upon Ulster.

The South of Ireland became an independent Catholic republic. Ulster got its own gimmicky (and Protestant) form of Home Rule. Belfast became the capital of Northern Ireland. The majority status of Northern Ireland's Protestant community asserted itself from the outset and the first representatives elected to the province's parliamentary assembly at Stormont were overwhelmingly Unionist Protestants.

For nearly fifty years, Ulster seemed quiet. It was the ignored South Africa in which a third or more of its population fretted under denominational apartheid. Catholics were disenfranchised by their faith. It was strange that the world was so surprised when the province finally blew its lid in the late Sixties. The previous forty or fifty years seem to me to have been heading only one way.

In those years, as the prosperous heat of Belfast's economic and industrial boom waned so drastically, I believe that the city found itself increasingly incapable of supporting the size of its population. That population had been created for and by the massive spurts of rapid industrial growth of the past. A large Belfast poor was thus inevitable and the worst dispossession occurred, predictably, among the Catholic minority. A situation as inequitable as this could not have been secure for long. As a growing population fought to reap the shrinking dividends from the declining city, conflict was ultimately predictable and widespread poverty even more assured.

THREE

Marty Murray lived in Ballymurphy in West Belfast. His two-bedroomed house was only thirty years old but already it seemed to be falling down around him. Cracks and gaps afflicted every wall and patches of damp appeared everywhere, like maps. On the kitchen wall was a devotional plaque representing some female saint in prayer. Marty carved it himself. It was a beautiful thing. When I told Marty that it looked like something El Greco might have done, Marty was pretty unimpressed. He seemed to think it was no big deal and hadn't heard of El Greco anyway.

Marty lived there with his wife, Ann, and two of their four remaining children. Two of their sons had been killed in their teens. One had been murdered by nationalist paramilitaries in circumstances which Marty did not want me to disclose, the other had died in a car crash. Their eldest son lived in England where he was prospering as a manager in a large retail company. Their eldest daughter lived in Edinburgh with her teacher husband. The two children who remained with them, a teenage boy and girl, were both still at school.

Marty was a slight, dapper man with his hair sharply parted and smeared back with hair oil. He wore dark suits and ties and sometimes looked like a pall-bearer. This lugubrious effect was at variance with his character which was jocose and energetic. He worked in a social club in another party of the city (another Catholic area). He worked four nights a week and all day Saturday. He received about £58 per week. In addition, Ann worked as a cleaner in the Royal Victoria Hospital on the Falls Road. She was paid just over £32 for her eighteen-hour week.

Obviously this net total of £90 per week was not enough to maintain the family of four. The children could not work since both parents were insistent that they continue their education as far as they possibly could. Topped up with Housing Benefit and Income Support, the family's weekly income was just short of £120 per week. Effectively, after rent, fuel and food bills, this meant an allowance of around £7 per family member per week to cover all other expenses.

This didn't seem a hell of a lot. What did they do for clothes, shoes, soap, toothpaste, books for the children, prescriptions, bus fares, telephone calls to their other two children? What did they do for entertainment, relaxation, holidays, newspapers, the odd night out? When I asked them they looked blankly back at me. They seemed embarrassed for me that I had asked such a foolish question. They didn't do any of those things.

Apart from their shoes, everything that their son and daughter wore was second-hand. This might be fashionable for the Oxbridge undergraduate but it is a sore humiliation for a sixteen-year-old Belfast schoolgirl. Tracy, the daughter in question, was bright and pretty but even I could detect that she didn't seem to dress in quite the same way as the other sixteen-year-old girls I saw around the city. Although she was normally expansive with me, she didn't mention this but I got the impression that her clothes were close to a badge of shame for her.

Paul, the seventeen-year-old, didn't seem terribly put out by the provenance of his wardrobe but he confessed to me in a private moment that his lack of cash was making him something of a pariah among his friends. The boys he knew at school were now at the age when their friendship continued its course outside the school. They drank in pubs, they went to concerts and to the cinema. Paul could not afford to do that. He attended a grammar school and the other sixth-formers were mostly middle-class boys who had a decent allowance. Paul could only afford to be a school-time friend with them.

Marty and Ann were proud of their gifted, clever children. It formed the main preoccupation of their life. They told me that they wanted Tracy and Paul to avoid the plight of the other young people of the estate who congregated every evening around the street-lamps, tight in their festive but purposeless cliques. Marty and Ann endured many privations and made many sacrifices to ease their children's path towards some approximation of prosperity. Revealingly enough, they considered that their children would have their best chance in life if they left West Belfast, indeed Northern Ireland in general.

This is a common attitude in West Belfast. It was a notion I was familiar with in my own childhood and it endures now in spite of the considerable reduction in Ulster's yearly death toll. This indicates that the parents' general wish that their offspring should leave has perhaps less to do with Belfast's political violence than with the prevalence of economic deprivation and continuing decline. Marty certainly took something like this view.

'There's just nothing for them here any more. The kids leaving school haven't a chance of anything but the dole or some shite ACE Scheme [a form of job training scheme]. It's no future for them. Those schemes are a joke. Eight youngsters and some priest in a shed up the Whiterock talking about precision engineering. I don't want to see my Paul and Tracy ending up like that. Our Sean [his eldest son] has done well for himself because he went to England. He wouldn't have had the same opportunities here. This town is dead and buried.'

Turf Lodge, Ballymurphy, Clonard, Andersonstown, the Falls, Twinbrook, Poleglass. It reads like a roll call of the seditious, factious Irish. Two steps away from the moutain's edge, these areas are tucked away from the city's sight with less success than elsewhere. They haven't managed to circumnavigate West

Belfast entirely. That's one of the things about Belfast, its class divisions are shaky and flimsy. Folk from the Malone Road (Belfast's Kensington) aren't ignorant of the poverty of their dispossessed neighbours. This is mostly because these neighbours are only about five minutes down the road. Another reason, however, is that any journey in or out of the city takes you through some kind of poor area. You can't blink and miss it.

The denizens of West Belfast are the main players in Belfast's necrophiliac carnival. Their condition is dramatized whether they want it so or not. Since I came back to Belfast from England, I've taken some of my English friends into this area. It has been, almost without exception, exciting for them. They tell me that they felt special in those streets – they felt cinematic, theatrical or just plain epic.

A lot of people from West Belfast will tell you that they are weary of the constant scrutiny afforded to West Belfast. They will tell you that it's not a particularly bad or dangerous place. They will mention the fact that a lot of good people live there. They will say that, fundamentally, West Belfast is just like anywhere else.

This is a lot of crap. Many good people *do* live in West Belfast and, curiously enough, it *isn't* a particularly dangerous place. But West Belfast is not just like anywhere else. West Belfast is a very different thing.

I could reel out the statistics for you. We could easily talk numbers. Most depressed area in Western Europe, highest concentration of the jobless in Great Britain, poorest housing conditions in this country for fifty years, etc. It wouldn't prove much since it seems that statistics can tell you more or less what you want to hear. They are strangely treacherous allies.

I prefer to tell you what you might see if you took a trip up there one day. A Baedeker piece.

Poleglass, Twinbrook, the Falls, Andersonstown, Clonard, Ballymurphy, Turf Lodge. These areas form a rind around the lean meat of the city centre and the commerce of Boucher's

Road. The area is not quite a satellite of the city but it forms a restless scrub land that fades away from central Belfast into the very foot of the Black Mountain.

Although this forms a region economically depressed on a scale it is hard to describe, the area can still be beautiful. The sky can quickly grow awe-inspiring. The first ten years of my own life were spent in the radius of Turf Lodge, the very end of the city, the elbow of the arm of West Belfast as it turns alongside the mountains. The estate seemed radiant to me as a child. The pebbledash and pale brick of Turf Lodge lent it the air of a dusty *pueblo* like the ones in which my favourite television cowboys strode their manful. There seemed no want of glamour and resonance in Turf Lodge's rubble and trouble.

Some of this still lingers with me. But now when I'm in West Belfast, I notice things I never saw before. I notice how the shops are sparse and poor. I notice the decaying or non-existent amenities. I can see that the *pueblo* streets are badly built and crumbling already. I see the clutches of aimless youths grouped on street corners in a different light. They are no longer mysterious and attractive cliques I wait to join, but some kind of symptom of purposelessness and poverty of resource and income.

And yet West Belfast is still comely and admirable. The marginal or stricken status it enjoys does not rob the region and its people of their stature and their integrity. A lot of bad stuff goes down in West Belfast, devastating deprivation and decay prominent among it, but still West Belfast more than survives. West Belfast does not endure. West Belfast prevails in some way. It's a pretty good trick considering its many qualifications for collapse.

Marty Murray seems almost prosperous compared with some of his neighbours. His home, though structurally disastrous, is warm and comfortable. His family's poverty has not torn them apart, their support and care for each other continue in the face of their deprivation and in some instances the family binds tighter together to see off some of the worst effects of their financial circumstances. Marty sticks to a notion of working-class striving and respectability that seems to have grown out-dated elsewhere. His trim jacket and tasteful ties seem a retort against his conditions. He knows better than most I met that his circumstances are deteriorating critically and have done so for a decade or more.

'A few years back we were bringing in more or less the same kind of money. It got us much more then. It actually made a bit of a difference. We weren't rich but we got by much better. The problem is that the money's still the same all these years later but it seems to buy us nothing. It's wild, boy. It's like it's a completely different amount even though the numbers are the same. We never thought that this was going to happen. I mean the politicians were telling us that inflation was a thing of the past and now we're nowhere. The cost of living's gone out of our control and we can't even make a dent in bills and stuff like that.'

Ten years ago, a strange thing was happening. Then, it seemed to me, as a teenager, that an income of £100 per week was an astoundingly prosperous sum. The digits seemed chunky and indefatigable in their plenty. £100 was a mental barrier between approximate hardship and approximate plenty. This three-figure Plimsoll Line between hardship and munificence has been passed but the memory lingers. It is still hard to shake the conviction that a family of four receiving just over £100 per week are having it pretty easy. This is, needless to say, a fantas-tic notion. £100 per week for more than two people doesn't even trouble the scorers, it doesn't get you on the runway never mind off the ground. It's Dickens's farthing, Thackeray's shilling. As Marty says, it's nowhere money. The appearance of prosperity that lingers round the sum is a relic of vanished times.

But even Marty didn't have it as bad as Patsy, a woman who lived a couple of streets distant. Patsy and her husband were both jobless. They lived in a tiny, squalid house with little heating but much damp. Patsy's husband, Ronnie, hadn't worked for more than ten years and Patsy had worked only temporarily and mostly part time in that period. Their combined benefit just covered their rent and fuel bills and left a dainty sum for food and other living expenses of £25 per week. Patsy and Ronnie didn't do much dining out. After years of increasing hardship, Patsy had started selling their saleable belongings, the odd piece of furniture or some decent garment. They were old hands at the penny-a-word small ads in the *Belfast Telegraph*. It had been at least a couple of years since they had anything left to sell.

They were among the poorest people I had met. Ronnie, at the age of fifty-seven, had little hope of finding a job in Belfast. Patsy would only ever find badly paid temporary or part-time work. Their situation, barring truly unforeseen miracles, could never really improve. As the purchasing power of their benefit continued to slide irrevocably, they were realistic about the prospect of their future and worsening hardship. They coped with this by expecting little or less.

Patsy's pensioner mother was a regular presence in the house. She shared many of Patsy's features and some of her indomitable characteristics but she was often querulous and confused. She managed her pension poorly and was sometimes an extra burden on her daughter who would have to invite her to share meals with her and her husband. Patsy was almost in the position of being a home-carer without receiving the concomitant benefit. Somehow she managed to support herself and her two dependants on the less than little she had. I don't think Patsy was quite sure how she managed it either.

There were many people in Patsy's neighbourhood who suffered under similar constraints. They too somehow 'managed'. However, their 'managing' was sometimes a fairly rudimentary way of keeping themselves and their families alive. Bare existence was managed but the lengths to which people were driven to 'manage' were absolutely astonishing to hear about, never mind actually endure. In this end of poverty people had to do amazing things. Their diet was entirely dictated by how much bulk was affordable for the least money. Modish notions of wholefood or high-protein regimes were impossible to fulfil. Bread wasn't just the staff of life in Ballymurphy, it was the sandals and the robe as well. People boiled rather than fried their food. Water was much cheaper than oil or lard. Potatoes, cheap and adaptable, were ubiquitous to the point of monotony. Meat when it was available came in the form of the cheapest cuts possible or the coarsest mince. Lean meat, recommended by every quack in the western world, was simply too expensive. Wholegrain rice was dearer than white. Vegetables were surprisingly expensive since local shops were small and transport to supermarkets difficult. There is some substance to the claim that this bad diet is a cultural phenomenon. Certainly, there is still some suspicion about new ways of eating: my father, a Falls Road man in essence, refuses to dine in my home. On the other hand, economics plays a major role in the diet of the poor. The middle classes tell us that healthy food is cheaper but it often seems to depend on living in an area affluent enough to have the requisite kinds of shops, or else having a car to get there. Also try telling a Turf Lodge matron that the purchase of a wok or a garlic press is an essential one. You'd get small change, I fear.

People seemed to buy many of their clothes, towels, bedding and suchlike from Primark in the city centre, a large department store which sells its goods at sometimes astonishingly low prices made possible by its rapid turnover. There are quite a few establishments like this – Poundstretchers and, of course, Argos. Woolworths has some decent prices and a new shopping centre called the Park Centre has been built near the Falls Road. But such opportunities are by no means available to all. They offer little comfort to those families with young children who need new clothes almost every few minutes.

Unscientifically, I would claim that half or more of the people I spoke to in West Belfast were in debt. Most struggled under growing rent arrears which no amount of instalment paying seemed to dent noticeably. Fuel poverty was widespread and everyone seemed to be in arrears with their electricity or gas bills. I got the impression that once any of these families fell into arrears with any of these types of payment they were caught in a trap from which they could not escape, try as they might. Their benefit was designed for crisis management. It was meant to be enough to allow them to just scrape through until the next payment. In a situation like that, proper budgeting or fiscal wisdom is impossible and payment of outstanding debts is a hollow joke. This was exacerbated by one-off social security grants for large items like beds, cookers or fridges having been replaced by the one-off loans system, the Social Fund.

Indeed, source deductions from benefit to cover all types of arrears were not uncommon. I even met one man who was paying off a magistrate's fine by having his benefit docked before he received it. He had not been consulted about this and had no choice but to accept it. I was reminded of Hally from Kingsmead. Arrears had done for him pretty thoroughly. I didn't bring this example up in Belfast. It would have been a little pessimistic, I felt.

Pensioners fared both better and worse than had been my understanding of how they coped in London. Housing for the elderly in West Belfast seemed to be of a pretty high standard in the main. The organization and resources available to the social services to deal with them are, if not greater than in London, at least, more wisely used. There were the same problems with mobility, heating and access but such issues seemed to be more sensitively handled.

This is not to say that the pensioners of West Belfast were in Easy Street. I met an elderly woman called Agnes Murtagh in Turf Lodge who had not cooked a meal for herself since the previous year. This wasn't due to frailty or indolence. She simply didn't have a cooker. Her previous cooker had breathed its last the summer before and she had found it impossible to find anyone who would provide her with a new one. The Social

Fund administrators for her area told her that their limited budget had been expended and no more money was available for more than a year. The various charities to which she was directed also failed to come up with anything since they had been swamped by needy claimants similarly rejected by the Social Fund.

West Belfast was full of snapshots of dispossession. Jennifer G. and her children ate rice and mushrooms six nights out of seven. Adele from Andersonstown heats a tiny room in her OAP's flat only three days a week and wears two coats in bed. A Clonard man's toddler son cries ceaselessly as he coughs blood in a room green with damp. Paul Bradley, a twenty-six-year-old fitter, trains for three years and goes on to work for only six weeks in the next seven years.

As I write this, I glance to my left and I see that I've got a list of these things. In fact, I've got two. One in a notebook and one on audiotape. Sketchy details of two score or more people whose lives had been rubbled by poverty. They are long, dull lists, as all catechisms really are. Una and Stephen plan to marry. They have one child, a one-year-old boy. They have never had a full-time job between them and believe they never will. They promise themselves fantastic advantages and privileges for their son. Bobby Martin is an unemployed, middle-aged married man with grown-up twin sons. He suffers from a serious heart condition and has no possibility of employment with his health problems. His disability benefit keeps him fed and housed but his wife's benefit has been reduced and the couple struggle to cope. Bobby had an argument with a local youth who had been brawling outside their home: their windows are now broken regularly and Bobby has been threatened and jostled often by the young man and his friends. A couple from Twinbrook who did not want to be identified in any way can no longer afford to support their four children. For three years they have struggled to endure mounting rent and fuel arrears along with shrinking income and benefit. They are now considering voluntarily placing their children, whom they love with a visibly fiery, desperate ardour, into care. They can see no other solution. Soon they will not be able even to feed them. The woman has tried to commit suicide twice in the last six months. Her partner's eyes are glassy and dead with despair.

Tell yourself that it has to be like this. Tell yourself about economic and fiscal realities. Tell yourself about the trickledown theory. Tell yourself that the poor will be always with us.

How can we be happy with this? How *can* we?

I'm conscious that this may seem a little shoddy. A little flimsy or undisciplined. There doesn't seem to be much insight in such cheap emoting. I'm conscious of a lack of substance here. Where are the facts? Where are the figures? Where's the evidence? It's a common cry whenever criticism of the plight of Britain's poor is brought to bear.

With this in mind, I spent much time compiling sets of statistics. It started when I was considering the housing conditions in Hackney. By the time I'd been back in Belfast for a couple of months I had amassed quite a pile of statistics, graphs and pie charts. Donovan thought that I was missing the point. He asked why I used statistics to bolster writing that was supposed to be about what I saw and felt. The important facts were what I witnessed, not those which could be upholstered by a smattering of figures. Donovan told me that I must write what I saw, that I must bear witness.

All very well but already, even as I write now, I'm missing my stats. The unsettling aspect is that I hadn't really realized how much I had been enjoying my statistics. They seemed so sure, so easy and certain. A problem solved and an opinion made all through the offices of some squat little numbers followed by that reassuringly chubby percentage sign. I mean look at it – % – even without any accompanying numbers, you still feel slightly awed by its bilious authority. In reality it's a meaningless piece of typography and, sadly for us all, tragically for any ideal of governmental rectitude, the numbers that tend to precede that tyrannous sign have themselves become increasingly meaning-less. In the face of the misguidance, inaccuracies and downright lies committed with the help of the percentage, we have to preserve the idea of how important one's own observations and impressions are. Particularly when those observations and impressions directly contradict the leagues of confident numbers as they so often seem to.

Statistics have been a great growth industry since the early to mid nineteen-eighties. Margaret Thatcher's successive admin-istrations were at the forefront of this explosion in the numerate sciences. It was a simple but brilliant idea when someone in government realized the solution to discouraging statistics: if a set of statistics persisted in rising, falling or remaining stationary contrary to government wishes, they could simply be tampered with so that they began to toe the line. Statistics were not inviolate. They were not hewn into the rock of incontrovertible truth. If statistical tinkering was complex enough, protest could only be muted. Who could fully understand such intricate math-ematical manoeuvring? How likely was a public outcry about something as esoteric as the high science of statistical integrity?

It's difficult to write sensibly about statistics at the best of times and at the moment it is almost impossible to discuss them calmly. Particularly in the last two or three years, it has seemed to me that government statistics have become unwholesomely gymnastic. It must have seemed similar to you too. Nobody can really ignore it, can they? The manipulation has been too flagrant. The poor things have been compelled to jump through hoops, balance plates on their noses and stand on their hind legs in the most undignified fashion. For more than a decade, we have been ruled by a government who can cook the books enough to render palatable its disastrous economic policies, its record trade deficits, its productivity slides and irregularities in the Department of Trade and Industry. But perhaps the greatest liberties of all have been taken with those statistical details that deal with unemployment and poverty. The ambition there has been greater. In those fields, the number juggling has been intended to make both phenomena, poverty and unemployment cease to exist. We scarcely need examples. Surely even the most fervent supporters of free-market capitalism, or whatever, must feel some unease about official government poverty statistics. If they don't feel that unease, perhaps they should listen up some.

Probably the greatest attempt at statistical sleight of hand in Britain occurred in 1988. The Government decided to cease publishing figures on the scale of poverty in Britain which had shown a consistent and irritating rise since 1979. Such figures pointed the finger of blame much too squarely. The annual figures were replaced with *estimates* based on the incomes of 'Households Below Average Income' *relative* to the average national income. These new figures were first published in May 1988. Surprise, surprise, overnight the poor suddenly seemed to be improving their living standards much faster than the rest of the population. Cheekily enough, the new figures even directly contradicted separate government statistics released by the Department of Employment.

Then, an all-party Commons Social Services Select Committee found that 'the changes are likely to lead to an underestimate of the numbers on low income'. This didn't even cause discomfort. The other great Thatcherite innovation in parliamentary technique came into play – if you don't like a Select Committee finding you simply ignore it. Admittedly, this technique was really nothing new but the arrogance and frequency with which Margaret Thatcher employed it *was* truly revolutionary.

These wonderful new poverty statistics effectively discredited a series of indicators damaging to the administration. Suddenly, figures current in the mid-eighties which showed 9.38 million people on or below the poverty line (that is, Supplementary Benefit levels) were in question. They had painted a picture of a massive 17 per cent of the population, at least, suffering from poverty. These figures died in the night. Other DSS findings, including figures which indicated rises of 100 per cent and 120 per cent in child-related poverty, also conveniently bit the dust.

Even the miraculous disappearance of countless thousands of people from the unemployment figures has not been as daring as the above. Even in a period when the unemployment statistics underwent *twenty-four* changes of definition. The absurdity of YOP schemes, YTS or Restart had some remnant of shoddy logic. On the other hand, that great Circumlocution Office euphemism 'seasonally adjusted' unemployment was so absurd and transparent as to indicate real administrative contempt for the intelligence of the British public. Were we supposed mulishly to believe in that vaudevillian chimera? We didn't. I know one young man in London who used to sign on wearing a T-shirt which bore the legend 'I want to be seasonally adjusted.'

The first hole in the May '88 scam occurred when the Government got into a small controversy over the figures that they are compelled to release to the European Community (they can't cook those) which showed a *rise* of 1.5 million in Britain's poor. The definition of the poor for these purposes was those with less than half the average *disposable* income (around 12 per cent for Britain). True to style, Margaret Thatcher disputed that definition and those figures in parliament. She seemed unconcerned that they came from her own government.

The disgusting fiction of Thatcherite poverty statistics finally crumbled in April 1990. The Government was forced to withdraw the kind of official statistics that it had introduced in May 1988, only two years before. Their trickledown theory, whereby prosperity magically filtered down from the highly paid to the poor, was completely annihilated. The 'Households Below Average Income' calculations were humiliatingly discredited. The much repeated government contention that the poorest 10 per cent of the population had enjoyed the greatest increase in living standards was shown to be absolutely untrue by the parliament-appointed Institute of Fiscal Study. The Government was forced to admit that its figures had been 'misleading'.

Further embarrassment awaited. In July of the same year the Government had no choice but to publish figures showing that the poorest 10 per cent of the population had actually seen their real income *fall* by 5.7 per cent since Margaret Thatcher had become prime minister. In the same time average incomes had risen by 25 per cent. The figures were sneaked out to avoid newspaper and television news deadlines. Depressingly, the ploy worked fairly well. It was a remarkable story. It *is* a remarkable story. It is proof from the Government itself that it had massively distorted statistics on poverty, telling a story diametrically opposite to the truth. To me that sounds like a pretty good definition of lying. Falsehood, distortion and deceit.

At the same time, the Royal Statistical Society reported that public confidence in official statistics was dangerously low and the Society suggested that the Government's statistical office should be reformed to prevent political tampering with its work. Neither this finding nor the recommendation was debated in parliament.

Well, there you go. The Government lied. Repeatedly and without fear, the Government of Great Britain lied to its electorate. The Government got caught. And now the Government cannot escape the unwelcome task of telling us that under their aegis, the poor of Great Britain have grown much poorer while the rest of society has seen its living standards and expectations improve. Have you heard any cabinet minister acknowledging their sponsorship of this view? Me neither.

Even without the figures, even without the evidence or proof, even if you ignore the last two pages, you still know that the Government was lying. Of course you do. We all know that. It's an astounding phenomenon but I have never met anyone who believed what the Government said about unemployment figures or poverty-related statistics. Even those who were glad to tell me that they supported and endorsed the Conservative government's principles and practices, expressed total disblief in all its poverty stuff. Goodness, it actually requires a moment's thought to recognize what an extraordinary situation this is. We seem aware, resigned or content that we be governed by an administration that we know misleads us. We seem to be like liberal parents, indulging a favourite child's romancing. We seek to think that a little falsehood comes with the territory.

Call me politically naïve, but I fail to cope with this. The increase in hardship for the poor is not happening. The complaining deprived are liars and parasites. The witnesses, the bystanders who see and report the empirical evidence of deterioration are blind or mad or Marxist. The poor are better off than ever before. Titanic pay increases and tax cuts for the wealthy and prosperous are of material benefit to the poor. Unemployment is falling rapidly. Housing is fine. State benefit is higher than ever before and provides more than adequately for those in need. Homelessness is a little local difficulty. The National Health Service is now better than ever. Marty Murray is a liar. Gabrielle is a fool. Henry Richards is a whinge. Alan has got it all wrong.

How can we be happy with this? How *can* we?

FOUR

I was glad to be back in Belfast. The sum of what I was encountering there was as harrowing if not more so than that which had daunted me in London. But at least in Belfast I could go home every night. In addition, I knew much of Belfast as well as anyone and therefore, by definition, I scarcely knew other areas at all. (That's Belfast for you. Dictated by the creed under which you were born, you can know the regions in which your co-religionists live but you tend not to spend much time promenading in the other community's territory. Belfast isn't a very big city and yet I first set foot in Finaghy, Taughmonagh, Ballybeen and Tiger's Bay when I was twenty-six years old. I had walked the Shankill for the first time only a year earlier.)

Despite your best intentions, a new city's poorest areas or boroughs fill you with a kind of sweaty dread. You never feel quite comfortable there. You sense that you are under some kind of obscure but constant threat, which is generally more inimical to your peace of mind or your smug beliefs rather than your actual safety – but there is still much unease.

Most of the time I spent in Hackney was filled with this disquiet. No matter how well I came to know the area, how many people I met and liked nor how many nights I spent there, I was, none the less, anxious and uncomfortable. It was as though I was afraid that Hackney might somehow rub off on me.

Belfast was different. The larger part of what I knew of the city where I had lived were its poorest enclaves. Belfast's deprivation was the bricks and mortar of my childhood. Its associations were largely benign for me. It is difficult to fear or find alien the streets that made you.

Donovan was in a different position when he turned his attention to his native city. He had grown up in an attractive and prosperous middle-class area of the city. Admittedly it was more or less next door to sets of Nationalist and Loyalist ghettos and, as I've already said, no one in Belfast, middle class or otherwise, can truly avoid the evidence of deprivation in their city. Donovan had photographed the most depressed areas of Belfast before, but that had been in the process of doing other work. Though he knew that large areas of Belfast were poor and breaking down, the city for him was associated with prosperity and a degree of middle-class comfort that came directly from his background and upbringing.

We had different difficulties in understanding what we saw in unprosperous Belfast. I was in danger of complacency or familiarity, rendering the plight of such areas somehow tolerable or natural. Donovan ran the risk of not quite believing that the city which had nurtured him could be so cruel or bereft.

There was also the problem for me that there seemed no new way of saying what ailed West Belfast in particular. The predicament of those who lived in that slice of the city lent itself to the dramatic evocation or the righteously astounded polemic. But this was not the truth of how most people in West Belfast lived. People were happy or unhappy, striving and confident as much as they might have been anywhere. I was surprised at quite how tolerable so many people's lives seemed. This daunted me. I couldn't really write that everything was great in Andersonstown or Twinbrook. I didn't want to say that things were going extra-swimmingly for Belfast's least well off. On the other hand, I couldn't invent abnegation where it did not exist.

Pat O'Neill and his family live in a decent three-bedroomed house just off the Grosvenor Road. Pat and his wife, Sandra, have four daughters. The eldest is nineteen and the youngest is eight. The middle two are twelve and seventeen. Their home is marked by its multiply feminine occupancy – it is comfortable and elegantly furnished to an enviable degree. Pat himself even bears the stamp of the fatherhood of exclusively female children. His tastes and habits are mild and his manner amiable and pacific. He is an antidote to the surprisingly successful image of the West Belfastman as a crass, gun-crazed, bibulous ruffian. He is sensitive, sagacious and amusing.

Pat works in an engineering firm on the other side of the river Lagan in East Belfast. He does a complex and recondite job for which he is paid fairly well. Sandra also works part time in a local school and the net family income was the highest of anyone else featured in this book. Pat runs a car and the family has a caravan which they keep in a caravan park in Portnoo in Donegal. Their eldest daughter, Sarah, was taking a year off to accumulate some money before taking up the place at Newcastle University which she had been offered a few months before. Two of the other daughters attend St Dominic's, an excellent and successful grammar school for girls on the Falls Road. The youngest daughter, though still only at primary school, is exhibiting the same tendency and desire to extend her education.

Pat has been in his present job for just over three years. Before that, he was unemployed for more than eight years. Between 1974 and 1979 he worked for a different engineering firm in East Belfast. This firm employed an overwhelmingly Protestant workforce and was situated in a staunchly Loyalist area of the city. Pat was happy there: he enjoyed the work, was paid well and got on with his Protestant workmates from whom he received no sectarian 'hassle' as he put it. However, 1978 and 1979 saw another spate of sectarian murders of people who worked in areas of the city inimical to their religion. Several Catholics who worked for Protestant firms or in Protestant areas were butchered. When a Catholic man from Pat's own area was shot dead while going to work at a site only streets away from where Pat worked, he reviewed his situation. Though he felt comfortable with his Protestant colleagues and felt safe while actually at work, he could no longer guarantee his safety on his journeys to and from work. Pat's colleagues shared his opinion. They advised him to leave. Pat took this, wisely, to mean that they knew that some of their more violent co-religionists might have plans for him.

Pat's resignation was not the disaster it might have been. There was a firm off the Springfield Road which had openings for skilled workers such as Pat. He approached the firm, looking for work. Two days later, the firm announced large-scale redundancies made necessary by the collapse of a sum of investment capital which they had been confident of attracting. The investors had pulled out because they felt that a firm situated in West Belfast would have endemic problems with terrorism and intimidation and this was unacceptable to them.

'I was astonished,' Pat told me. 'There were only a handful of firms that I could work for in the city. I'd left one of them and another one wasn't able to take me on. Most of the other places I could have worked were in the Prod areas and Sandra wouldn't let me go back to working like that. In the last couple of months at —— [the firm Pat had worked for between 1974 and 1979] her nerves had been terrible bad. She was on Valium in the end and she was convinced that if I went to work for another Prod firm that I'd get shot for certain.

'And all the while, the Provies were claiming to be fighting for my best interests and yet it was on account of them that I didn't have a job. I mean without the troubles, I could have worked more or less anywhere I wanted. My father worked on the Shankill all his working life and he never had a minute's trouble. I know that us Catholics didn't maybe have the amount of jobs that we should have had in the fifties and the sixties and that, but, if anything, that kind of thing has got worse since the troubles started. Now, hardly nobody's got jobs. And I got sick and tired of Sinn Fein telling me that they were on our side when all they could do was make it more difficult for us. There were other ways to fight for our rights. All they can do is shit in their own nests. I mean, what area has done worst out of the troubles? West Belfast, of course. We were just shooting ourselves in the foot, or rather, the Provies were doing it for us.

'I was on the dole for eight years. I couldn't believe it. Sandra had just had Siobhan [their youngest child]. I mean, I didn't anticipate having to go on the dole, it hadn't been part of my plans. When Sandra had been pregnant with Siobhan, I'd been in a good job and we'd been bringing in good money. Suddenly, I had four kids and no work. Jesus, we were in a desperate state. Truly desperate.'

Pat and I were sitting in his sunny back garden as he was saying this. An inquisitive neighbour made her presence clear from over the garden fence and Pat lowered his tone which had grown truculent and impassioned. He winked at me and called a greeting to the woman who lived next door. We heard a brief scurrying and a door slammed shut as she retreated indoors. Pat went on, smiling.

'Anyway, where was I? Oh, aye. Them years were terrible bad. I'd never been out of work all the time Sandra and I were married and we'd never had to do without. We weren't rich but we had enough. I ran a wee car and we had the odd holiday of a summer. But now we had nothing. Supplementary Benefit was nothing – absolutely nothing. The first years wasn't so bad. I mean, we didn't have any money but I thought that it wouldn't be too long before I got another job. I tried to hold on to the car for as long as I could but I had to sell it after about a year. I couldn't pay the insurance or the road tax. Things were getting really bad then. Losing the car was a big blow for me. Before, when things had been getting on top of us, we'd pile the kids in the car and drive out into the country. We'd go to Millisle or Bangor or somewhere. That helped a lot. I missed doing that.'

Pat and I drank weak tea while he described in detail the lengths to which he and Sandra had to go to try to provide what they considered enough for their children. They sold whatever furniture or fittings that they had amassed when Pat was work-ing. Pat would fix a neighbour's car or household appliance for

BELFAST

Cavehill, from Rathcoole

Old and new housing, Springhill

Inadequate homes, Springhill

Interior, Springhill

Making toast, Ballybeen

Going home, Crumlin Road

Second-hand furniture store, Antrim Road

Woman in sunshine, Union Street

Weekday, Castle Street

Thompson, Rathcoole

Crescent, Rathcoole

Conversation, Duncairn Gardens

Labour Day, Lower Falls

Anniversary, Beechmount

Dereliction, Upper Shankill

Hostel kitchen, Lower Falls

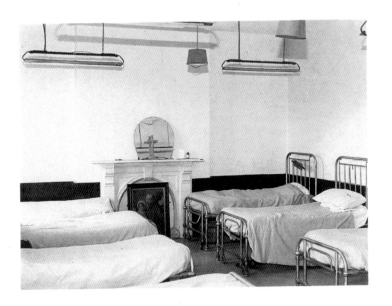

Hostel dormitory, Lower Falls

Shopping, Duncairn Gardens

Community, Beechmount

Elswick Street, Clonard

Early morning, Smithfield

Working man, North Belfast

Black taxi, Upper Falls

Faith, Andersonstown

a fiver or so. Sandra landed a job as dinner lady in a local primary school but the hours were limited and the pay poor. They were grateful that the children's education seemed to be unaffected by their new straitened circumstances. Sandra described how important this had become to them.

'I think that was the main thing that kept us going. After a couple of years, I began to think that Pat would never get another job. If it hadn't been for the children doing well at school, there'd have been nothing to hope for. Sarah was brilliant. She was at the age where she was wanting fashionable clothes like her friends at school had. But she was very grown-up about it. She knew we couldn't afford maybe what their parents could afford to spend on them and she never once complained or made us feel that we were letting her down. The other girls were good too. In some ways, it was better that we had the four girls because they helped around the house and made things easier for me and Pat. Boys mightn't have done that as much.'

This seemed the story that many parents had already told me – how their children had been their prop, inspiration and greatest comfort in dreadful circumstances. This is interesting, since some of the harshest criticism of Britain's poor centres on their continuing to bear children. Some folk seem to think that one should not procreate when one is poor. It is part of a lubricious and unwholesome idea that the private or sexual lives of the deprived are open to the investigation and interference of society's other classes. It conjures up an image of a sexually incontinent underclass in which the males repeatedly impregnate their females without due thought to income or future provision for their offspring. A myth persists that the 'lower classes' are somehow more promiscuous than their betters. Generalizations are always worthless and seductive in equal measure. I hesitate to make one, but my experience of sexual behaviour differences between classes certainly does not bear out this nightmare of the libidinous proletariat. I was born and brought up in working-class Belfast. When I was nineteen, I went to Cambridge

University. Up until then my experience of promiscuity had been theoretical or literary. At Cambridge, I was privileged to see the youth of Britain's upper-middle-class conduct its sexual business. I was astounded by what I encountered. Sex seemed an easy seamless thing. Youth of both sexes had notched up a greater aggregate of sexual partners by the end of their first year than most people in working-class Belfast would have managed in a lifetime's striving.

The sterilizing, compulsory birth control lobby would say, but this is childfree sex – a very different thing. At least these undergraduate women don't lumber themselves and the state with a couple of kids before they get out of their teens. The poor marry or cohabit and produce too many children too young. This they decry. This is what they cannot begin to understand. It would seem that two unemployed nineteen-year-olds who produce a child are making things even more difficult for themselves than they already are.

Early marriage and early parenthood among the poorest quarter of society is a phenomenon too widespread and too well observed to ignore. I believe that it is *not* inexplicable. There are many causes, reasons and inducements to early marriage and parenthood for the young poor. Young people who are living with their parents and perhaps a clutch of brothers and sisters undergo a multitude of stresses. The houses are usually small, space is limited and privacy impossible. When resources are limited, recreation is difficult and the family finds itself together at home more than would be the case in a more prosperous home. In such circumstances, while undergoing the private dramas and novelty of late adolescence, the youth's boyfriend or girlfriend can often seem the only avenue for real self-expression or moral autonomy. Marriage or childbearing at such an age brings disadvantages, it's true, but it also generally leads to an opportunity of setting up a home away from one's own parents and an escape from the suffocating restrictions of the overcrowded parental home.

However, this would not explain why so many impoverished

couples persist in having large or semi-large families. Three or four children brought up on Income Support or Family Credit seems to be an imposition on the delicacy of many commentators' feelings. From the outset, such faint moralizing is facile. There is no substance to claims that the poor should not have families. The desire to have several children is a private matter and not one which is in the remit of the middle-class castigators. Working-class or poor young women are known to have less effective access to information about contraception. The termination of an unwanted pregnancy is a much more cumbersome and difficult affair for a girl with a deprived background and particularly in Northern Ireland, where abortions are still illegal and where there may be considerable moral or religious pressure to give birth to an unwanted child. It is even difficult in Belfast to receive any real guidance in the matter of abortions since the various advisory services tend to gear their counsel towards avoiding abortions at all costs.

The benefits which poor families reap from having children are demonstrated with greater clarity as the children grow older. It's a weary old commonplace to say that parents who have enjoyed few privileges always try to allow their offspring the kind of advantages in life which they themselves missed. Among the poorest parents I met, the extent of emotional investment in their children's future was remarkable. They seemed to have extraordinary ambitions for their children and worked as hard as they could to make those aspirations feasible.

Gabrielle had endured sustained periods of blight solely for her children. Hally, his suite in Pentonville booked, was more murdered by the loss of his children than anything else. Donovan was full of stories of doting Blackhill parents hothousing their fractious offspring. Here in Belfast, I saw Moira from Clonard dream her children's future secure. Pat and Sandra O'Neill were churning out a quartet of intellectual demons from one of the most deprived regions in western Europe. Alan mourned that he could not take his proper place as father to his children.

The sons and daughters of these people were being groomed for a success or prosperity which had proved impossible for their parents. It was as though Gabrielle or Sandra O'Neill were ensuring that some trace of their spirit would go on to enjoy some of society's available boons. I imagine it made their own lack seem less galling or hopeless if they were confident that a part of their genetic selfhood would 'do better for themselves'. It is perhaps impossible to understand quite how much comfort or encouragement such a notion could provide for the impoverished parent.

Needless to say, it's not all like this. Often, a large poor family can be a disastrous aggregate of deteriorating factors. The incessant and increasing demands of children can overwhelm a needy parent. Children may be neglected or just inadequately loved or cared for. But this could be true of a family in any income group. Parental neglect, abuse or incompetence is not confined to the poor. It is curious that we think that everyone has the capacity for childcare. This is simply not the case. A considerable portion of our society is incapable of caring for their children properly. There are people who ideally should be dissuaded from parenthood.

However, it is impossible to ignore that while such latent unsuitability may not be determined by class or income, there *are* certain pressures and obstacles to easy parenthood which are exacerbated by poverty. The couple from Twinbrook who wished to be anonymous are a good example, the suicidal wife and ulcerous husband with their four pretty, amiable children. They wanted to keep their children more passionately than I can describe. When they spoke to me of their reluctance to place them into care, their words were inflamed, febrile. They were people whose parenthood wasn't just being *affected* by their poverty – their parenthood was being *destroyed* by poverty.

Being female packs poverty's punch. It puts lead in its gloves and fire in its belly. Being a woman and being poor is a big mistake. All the bad effects of deprivation are worse for women – *all of them*. And yet, investigations of poverty seem to hover so lovingly over male unemployment and the erosion of the old proletarian myth of the 'working man'. Poor women rarely seem to receive such sympathetic scrutiny. Their plight is often dismissed or underestimated. Additionally, multiple child bearing can seriously interfere with the freedom and autonomy of poor women.

Of course, women bear the worst brunt of dispossession. Childcare, perhaps the single greatest stress and difficulty increased by poverty, almost invariably falls within a woman's remit. Perhaps, the male single parent pushing a pram in his milk-stained chinos is a common sight on Hampstead Heath but, believe me, in Bethnal Green or Andersonstown, it would bring out the cameras; there would be press conferences, expert speculation.

Housing and maintenance of the home also seem to be the lot of women in poor areas. The handyman husband seems an entirely lower middle-class figure. Responsibility for keeping barely tolerable housing conditions remotely habitable falls continually on the kind of women I met. I encountered women who achieved astounding feats of DIY with a bent table knife and a ball of cheap string. There was a married woman from Beechmount, off the Falls, whose wiring abilities included repairing her own television and whose kitchen was stocked with appliances which she had rescued broken from dumps and restored to full electrical health through the exercise of her unusual gifts.

Provision of bedding, towels, household goods and suchlike rarely discomfited the husbands or partners of those women. Apart from Pat O'Neill in Belfast and Henry Richards in Hackney, I met no men who shared any of the tasks of cleaning the home with their wife or partner. They were comfortable in the thought that, like many prosperous folk, they had 'a little woman who does', with the difference that they were married to the little woman in question. Henry and Pat – two men out of countless scores.

Hah! Just as I write an elderly travelling woman has come

to the door. Gypsy woman, itinerant, call her what you will. She stood in a patterned dress and tried to sell me some sponges. I didn't want any. I also refused the scrubbing brushes, pan-scourers, tea towels and razors which she proffered from her supermarket shopping basket. I pleaded cashlessness but she didn't believe me. She told me that she needed money to feed her multitudinous children (she was at least seventy). I was tempted to spend a fiver. It seems that there are some cases when even the main thrust of the family's extra-mural entrepreneurial efforts are taken up by the women.

The family's diet, again with the noble exceptions of Henry Richards and Pat O'Neill, was the woman's sole concern. The purchase of foodstuffs with very small sums is an enviable skill as Donovan's experience with Norma in Glasgow proves, and many of the men I met had not really attempted to master it. Indeed, in the worst cases, the only contribution that the adult male made to the family's diet was to make it worse by dipping into the family's food money for some frivolous reason gener-ally involving gambling or alcohol. Flagrant abuse of this kind was not as common as some people imagine, but it was there. When spending some time in the New Lodge, a Catholic area of North Belfast, I went drinking with a thirty-six-year-old father of five called Joe McGinn. Before we left, there was a brief altercation with his wife which made plain that he had commandeered some cash which she intended to use for food. When we were in the bar, I tried to buy whatever drink that was to be bought. Joe would have none of this and made sure that he bought his rounds and more. He even invited two other men to drink with us so that they might 'help' me with my project and he stood them drinks repeatedly as well. No matter how hard I tried to bear the main expense of the evening's booze, Joe would outspend me in the most extravagant manner.

By the time I left, I had woozily calculated that he had spent a sum well in excess of £15, perhaps more than £20. I don't like beer and it had slid down my throat even less comfortably than usual that night since I could only remember that I was without doubt pissing away a substantial portion of the family's food-stuffs for the week. That Joe should have done such a thing is perhaps explicable. Maybe he couldn't bear the idea of me swanking away, buying drinks and patronizing left, right and centre but this was more than foolish – this was iniquitous, shameful, unforgivable.

I scarcely have to say that the women in poor families seem to do all the cooking. Well, anyway, the women in poor familes seem to do all the cooking. Fish swim, birds fly, women cook. An observation of such patent predictability doesn't merit a lengthy paragraph. That's how it is.

What do the men do? you ask. A good question. What do the men do? They do what they can get away with. That's what they do. That's what men will always do.

The men of West Belfast are given time by their women. They aren't exactly given ease, they're mostly too *actually* poor to get close to ease but they are definitely given time. The men there seemed to maintain a social life that was impossible for their women. West Belfast is littered with social clubs where men spend their time in each other's company. I don't claim that these are exclusively male preserves but I would certainly assert that they are *predominantly* male resorts. Deprived or job-less men in West Belfast can continue to enjoy the society of their friends and acquaintances. West Belfast women seem to have nowhere near the same opportunity for socializing as their men. Their main arena for comradeship tends to be in their workplace if they have one or simply with the other women who live in their immediate vicinity. The cliché of the streetful of matrons swapping support and stories across the doorsteps survives still. It's inaccurate but enduring.

It is remarkable that the men can do this sort of thing when they are in the grip of economic deprivation. A life under poverty has dynamics which other lifestyles do not share. Most of us have periods, however brief, when we can put our lives and careers in neutral and let them freewheel along while we take a break, a holiday or just a rest. We come back to our lives and find that they are still there. The job is there. The house is there. Nothing has gone badly wrong while we were away or distracted. In poverty, it is hazardous to take your eyes off the road or your hands from the wheel for an instant. A life of poverty requires absolute vigilance and constant wariness. The briefest inattention can wreak havoc. You glance back and find that your life has abruptly collapsed or detonated. A debt has spun out of control, an eviction notice has arrived or a social worker is telling you that your children are being sodomized. You can't rest, you can't relax. You can barely blink.

Men can roll along almost blithely sometimes, while their spouses flick their eyes over the immediate future, trying to spot and neutralize hazards that are still some way off and therefore manageable in scale. You don't need documentary evidence or statistics for a cultural and moral truth as spectacularly apparent as this. Married or cohabiting men or those who continue to live with their mothers have the worst stabs of their poverty blunted by the energy and stamina of the women in their life.

In her fine book, *Wigan Pier Revisited*, Beatrix Campbell is blunt about this imbalance:

Women are the poorest of all. It's an open secret. We protect men from the shame of their participation in women's poverty by keeping the secret . . . When a man lives [with a woman], a woman's independence – her own name on the weekly Giro – is automatically surrendered. The men become the claimants and the women their dependants. They lose control over both the revenue and the expenditure, often with catastrophic results: rent not paid, fuel bills missed, arrears mounting. It is conventional wisdom among advice agencies, local authorities and fuel boards that it's the women who pick up the tabs for the men's mismanagement.

Women are the poverty managers. They are the group who make poverty surviveable. In their coping with the weekly or fortnightly crises that are poverty's main product, they perhaps do themselves the ultimate disservice. If they can manage to scrape by despite their deprivation then it rapidly becomes morally tolerable for the rest of us. Indeed, it allows for further reductions in the ideal of what resources the poor should or could manage to survive with. Their making do also means that men are unlikely to change their own habits and disrupt a situation that is so overwhelmingly to their benefit.

And what benefit accrues for these women from their struggle? I asked a couple of women from Ballymurphy what they thought they gained from all the energy they put into supporting their families. Both were uneasy with such a question and obviously felt that they were being mocked. One told me that she did it because she loved her children and felt a duty towards her husband. The other simply said: 'That's all very well for you to say. But who would do it if I didn't?' That didn't seem much of a reason and the previous explanation, although undeniably heartwarming, seemed rather convenient. These women's experience of poverty was made more difficult by the men in their lives. There can be no doubt that without the disruptive and destructive presence of their men, these women's lives would have been considerably more prosperous and ordered.

It would appear that these women suffer great deprivation because they live with men. They are almost hampered by their heterosexuality. As a man, I'd like to be able to claim that the company and love of men would be worth such extra difficulties. I'm not sure I can. After the passage I have just quoted, Campbell goes on to examine exactly what benefit these women's sexual lives bring. She asks the women whether they have orgasms, whether they have heard of the clitoris or whether they find sex satisfactory. Campbell gets a straight set of negatives. She concludes that often ' . . . women's problem was heterosexuality. Sex hasn't changed, men haven't changed enough and motherhood shrouded in poverty is what it always was – gains and losses.'

I fervently hope that Bea Campbell never makes it to West

Belfast. She'd be steaming. West Belfast is still the land of the vaginal orgasm – East Belfast, middle-class Belfast, educated Belfast are the same. This is not as frivolous as it might seem. Since poor women are made poorer by sharing their lives with men, the question of their sexuality becomes vital. If independence or autonomy for women is attainable it must tackle the inequities of the major gender difference with men. A woman cannot achieve freedom or equality if the core of her sexual nature is ignored or gainsaid by men.

To be honest, I didn't really have the balls to ask the women I met about the quality of their sex lives but from the hints dropped or the details volunteered, I got the impression that they weren't ideal. I would have been wary of commenting on what they said about sex if I had not already witnessed so many of their spouses at play: goosing waitresses, cajoling young women and telling me what they wouldn't do to whatever attractive girl happened to pass within our field of vision.

Among the dispossessed, it seems that women are the poor relations. They are further dispossessed. They are dispossessed of their very womanhood. Sexual sedition is risky. Boys' nights out are commonplace. Girls' nights aren't uncommon but are carried out within strict limits. One glamorous middle-aged woman from Taughmonagh told me that she went out with her female workmates every other Tuesday. Her husband 'permitted' this on the understanding that she return home religiously before ten thirty. She had been late on several occasions. Her husband had started ripping up her clothes at exactly half past ten, continuing until she finally arrived. He offered her no violence (he scarcely needed to) but told her that in future, he would commence such destruction at ten thirty if she had not come home and continue it until she did return. Needless to say, this woman was now rarely late.

And Northern Ireland seems a very special case. Chauvinism and oppression of women in Ulster is quite exceptional in some ways. When I returned to my native city after living in England for six years, I was astonished by what I found. After associating with the educated, middle-class, vocal women I had known in England, Belfast shocked me. If England had given me anything, it had given me at least a vague hold on scrupulous sexual politics. Such niceties were surplus to requirements when I came back to Northern Ireland. Even women in social or economic groups normally associated with feminism, or at least fairly radical ideas of their own role, seemed but pale in their commitment to women's rights. Women graduates from Northern Ireland's universities seemed unconcerned by their poor access to a graduate labour market overwhelmingly dominated by male graduates often with much poorer qualifications. Actions and statements which would have been greeted with a storm of protest in London were permitted or tolerated here. I watched countless intelligent confident women listening without complaint to the old clichés of female inferiority being rehearsed without embarrassment.

Northern Ireland is only a special case in the sense that women's marginalization is simply more overt. The factors that exist in somewhere like Belfast – men's ignorance, fear or scorn – are commonplace throughout Britain but in Northern Ireland they are much less hazardous to promote. This is particularly true of the poorest areas of the city. Again, the difference is only one of degree or acceptability. Hatred or contempt of women and claims of male supremacy are just easier to get away with.

The openness of poor women's dispossession has a much more *actual* or empirical effect than is the case in other income groups. In practical terms, men use their licence to abuse in heaping greater trials upon the women in their lives. Whether it's marital violence (half a crime, I'm told), the onus of child-care, budgeting, housekeeping, cooking or home maintenance, women's extra poverty load is made possible by the essential proletarian myth of their men's supremacy. A confident counterpart of the middle-class notion of male supremacy.

This is not to say that the women of West Belfast are docile or supine. Nothing could be further from the truth. The working-class women of Belfast are famously vocal and combative. Most people are familiar with the television images of the Northern Ireland conflict in the 1970s – images of implacable working-class women banging bin lids and mercilessly haranguing the teenage soldiery. As a child in West Belfast, it seemed to me that Turf Lodge was an almost matriarchal society. The men were the marginal figures, always invisibly drinking in their dark pubs; or crowding betting shops, or populating the Government's latest internment centres. The community groups that seemed most constructive appeared to be staffed by my schoolfriends' terrifying mothers. I know for certain that most of the young British soldiers who patrolled our area intermittently feared the women much more than the men.

The poorest women of Belfast display their strength and stamina by hugely diluting the worst effects of whole regions' experiences of deprivation and violence. Their stature is clearly evident in that so many families and communities can survive such appalling circumstances with such meagre resources. West Belfast is, in the truest sense, run by West Belfast's women. But somehow, this strength, stamina and stature seems to stop short when it comes to dealing with their men.

And yet, there are many celebrated radical working-class women from Belfast or Northern Ireland, figures like Sadie Patterson, famous within their own communities for the selflessness and courage with which they pursued the cause of women's rights. Joyce MacCartan, whose own family has suffered terrible losses due to political violence, runs a successful women's drop-in centre on the Lower Ormeau Road. She dispenses information, encouragement and support to the women who come to it.

Traditionally, those voices raised most noticeably against Northern Ireland's political violence have been women's. The most visible of those movements was started in 1976 by two working-class women, Betty Williams and Mairead Corrigan. Indeed, the movement was popularly known for some time as

'The Peace Women'. A special non-combatant status is some-times given to the women of Belfast. They are seen as the mothers or wives of those who fight and die. It's a backhanded compliment to be sure, but it goes some way towards acknowl-edging that women in their province tend to exemplify an alternative to the tenets of violence and counter-violence.

Bernadette McAliskey was a celebrated radical figure in the earliest days of Northern Ireland's present political conflict. Press attention focused mainly on her nationalist views to the detriment of the considerable efforts she was making in the pursuit of women's rights. Nell McCafferty is one of Northern Ireland's finest commentators on a whole range of issues and much of her most acute insight and greatest energy is devoted to an examination of the imposed conditions of women in the North of Ireland.

And these women are only the most visible parts of a more general and organized women's movement in Belfast. There are self-help and support groups for women throughout the most impoverished quarters of the city. Belfast is abundantly scattered with such centres where women congregate to share their griev-ances or receive pragmatic advice or aid. And yet Belfast's poor record in women's rights persists regardless. Why?

I believe that the women's movement in Belfast is hampered by its queasy association with Republican politics. I know that many of the women I spoke to from Protestant Taughmonagh and Rathcoole felt that the women's movement was a predomi-nantly Catholic and Republican movement. Obviously, this was anathema to them. They rightly pointed out that it was strange for women who were supposed to be fighting for their gender's freedom to espouse immersion in a state (the Irish Republic) which outlaws contraception, never mind abortion. And apart from such considerations, many felt that they could not sacrifice their ideal of loyalism to the Crown for any notion of feminine self-determination.

Thus, the base of the women's movement is enormously diluted by sectarian complications. The workers' movements in the city are similarly affected. The Workers' Party, which sees itself as representing the workers of both communities, is prevented from having broad appeal by its lingering association with what was once the official wing of the IRA. The various manifestations of women's movements do not suffer such direct association but the presentiment prevails and that is enough to alienate the Protestant women of the city.

Helen Watson continues to support her jobless husband and her three teenage children (two unemployed sons and a daughter still at school) with the salary from her job as a nursing auxiliary and the Unemployment Benefit that her husband and sons receive (most of which they keep for their own use). In addition to working an average of fifty hours per week, Helen cooks, cleans, shops, launders, clothes and budgets for the family. Her face is lined and crossed by wrinkles and the flesh under her eyes is bruised with anxiety and exhaustion. When I asked her why she did so much, she answered pragmatically that if she did not do all that she did then no one else would.

'I have tried to get Jim or the boys to do a bit more but it always turns into a shouting match and even if they *do* help out a bit it only lasts for a day or two and then it's back to normal. I'd rather do without all the bad blood and the fighting and arguing and just get on with it. And it's not as if our Janine [her daughter] doesn't want to give me a hand when she can but she's doing so well at school and she doesn't get much support from her dad so I like her to do her homework before she does anything else.

'It does get on top of me sometimes. Sometimes I begin to think that it's not worth it and I just want to give up or have someone look after me. Sometimes, I just stop what I'm doing and cry. But most of the time it's all right – I mean there's plenty of women on this estate who have it worse than me. I mean, I've got a job and none of my sons is involved in any organization or anything like that. It isn't easy but then the women always have it hardest wherever they are.'

★

148

Women make poverty possible. Without women, poverty would be more intolerable than it already is. Poverty might well collapse entirely. Men are never going to make things easier for women. As Nell McCafferty says, 'Men aren't going to hand me my rights on a plate'. And those men who endure poverty are unlikely to change a situation that is so overwhelmingly to their advantage. Women in general must struggle for every small freedom to which they aspire. Women in poverty must struggle harder and endure more.

FIVE

Sometimes, looking out south from a window or street in Rathcoole, the mountains around Belfast seem to draw the mist and rain to themselves, effectively obscuring the city with their multiple soups. In certain light, the neighbouring mountains lose definition and dimension until they, too, look quite flat. Belfast's colour ebbs until a final lustreless blue over the hills is left to battle it out in the gunmetal sky. The mountains seem to control the weather. Clear or cloudy, it is often their decision. The buildings, the river and the people take their colour from the mountains' scheme.

Rathcoole is a massive, predominantly Protestant housing estate that spreads itself out as the main roads roll away from Belfast towards the north, Antrim, Carrickfergus and the international airport. It is trapped less than snugly between the Cavehill and the shores of Belfast lough. Isolated and stretched by its position, Rathcoole can feel like the end of Belfast or even a satellite of the larger city. It has all kinds of housing within its precincts. Much of Rathcoole, despite its predicament, remains austerely, dramatically beautiful. From Drumcree Place as the estate curves and climbs the approach of Cavehill, you can see one of the finest possible views of the city. The mountain itself is ever present, filling the prospect every time you glance north-west. The estate has a massive green space in its centre. It, I suppose, is supposed to be a vague parody of the village green or town square but ends up more a green square – a rectangular paddock of grass that seems both incongruous and fitting. Another parodic feature of the estate is a massive crescent of three-storey flats (now derelict) that were meant to resemble the pretty crescents in Bath or Parktown in Oxford. It was a nice idea but a disastrous reality. The only building occupied on the horseshoe block seems to belong to a local community project.

Dave Reid lives with his parents and two of his three brothers near Derrycoole Way. He is nineteen, a few months older than Donovan, he has not worked since he left school three years ago. He has worked on two different government training schemes for unemployed youths: once training as a joiner and finally as an auto-mechanic. Neither resulted in any greater opportunities for permanent employment. He now claims Unemployment Benefit again. He was not disappoined by the futility of his work on the training schemes, he expected nothing else.

'I don't know who they think they're fooling with these schemes. Everybody knows they're just to get the unemployment figures down. And it's not as if they're cheap. They have to employ people to run them and there's a lot of bureaucracy. I'm sure it costs more than it would if they just gave us all our dole money every fortnight. They're wasting good money on something just to make them look better and they have the cheek to tell us that they know how to handle money.

'Only a couple of the lads I was at school with have got a job now. All the rest of us have been through the schemes and on the dole and none of us, really, have found a full-time job. I've tried to get work on the other side of the city but as soon as they hear you're from Rathcoole, you've no chance. They either think you're some kind of head case or they think it's too far away if you don't have a car. The fellas in this estate who have good jobs have all got cars. Nobody wants to give you a job if it's gonna take you two buses and a wagon train to get in to work in the morning. I know a few people who work in Glengormley but there's nowhere near enough work there even though it's dead handy for the estate.'

Dave had been in trouble with the police twice in the past

six months and he noticed that he was beginning to get a reputation as a 'hood' (a Belfast term that covers youthful miscreants of all types not directly associated with paramilitary organizations). Dave protested that he was not a hood. He thought it was unfair that, young, jobless and male, people could imagine only one result for him – delinquency or petty crime.

'It's not as if I've done anything bad. I've been lifted a couple of times for fighting but I've never stolen anything and I've never been charged with anything. There are fellas on this estate who will provoke you into fighting and there's just no way you can avoid it. But the old women who live on my street think I'm Al Capone. It's just because I don't have a job and I'm not on a scheme. Jesus, few enough of their own sons have jobs. You'd think they'd have got used to it.'

Indeed, the example of Dave's neighbours' apprehension is surprising. A curious thing has happened in many of the poorest areas of Belfast: unemployment has lost its stigma. Northern Ireland is the land of no opportunity – employment vacancies are like griffins or unicorns, rare to the point of incredulity. In such circumstances, it is difficult to feel inadequate if you do not have regular employment. The chances are that most of the people you know will be in the same position. Joblessness is no longer shameful or unmanly. In some areas of Belfast joblessness is the prevailing state. If attempts to find work are so fruitless, do what you can, dignified unemployment must be your lot. 'Getting on your bike' to find work in this country involves migration to England or booking an international flight. The unemployed men and women of Belfast feel little shame. They cannot find work if there is no work to find.

There are several areas in Belfast where more than half of the area's residents are jobless. Rathcoole isn't as bad as some but it's still not great. Such widespread unemployment distorts the notion of time and affects how people tend to spend their days and weeks. Dave and his friends (all unemployed) fraternize most during the daylight hours when they are almost always together. Their group is much less often a plenum in the evenings. It is an enormous reversal of how most young men spend their time together – work or school during the day, leisure and companionship at night. The daylight/business/office hours appear to be the most onerous, the most difficult to pass alone. Dave certainly believed this.

'When we were all on schemes, we'd get together in the evenings. Even if we didn't go out somewhere, we'd meet in one of the boys' houses or just go round the estate together. We'd go looking for girls or something like that, or get a carry-out and have a few drinks. They used to be good nights we had. Now, we hang about together during the day. It's not that we had more money when we were on schemes – it's just that then we had something to do during the day. When you're on the dole, the daytime is the worst part, at least on weekdays. There's nothing happening on the estate, there's nothing on TV and everybody is getting chased out by their mothers or their girlfriends. So we just meet up and play pool in the club or go into the city centre and see if anything's happening down there.'

Dave's descriptions of how he spent his days seemed like exercises in futility. It's not that he or his friends were purposeless or apathetic; it's just that their circumstances invited tedium and restlessness. They were energetic, likeable young men, a good example of an unused and willing workforce with great talent and potential. They weren't even excessively cynical, which seems a true victory in the face of circumstances as unrewarding and hopeless as theirs. Their disbelief in the pedlars of governmental training schemes or 'restart opportunities' for the unemployed was scepticism rather than cynicism. It was a dignified refusal to believe in the new invisibilities and shibboleths of modern political science.

Dave was unique among them in that he believed he would never be given the opportunity to find permanent full-time work. The others persisted in believing that some kind of substantial up-turn in the economy would lead to a degree of prosperity in which they might share. In an unguarded moment,

I mentioned that I thought the idea of a population's full employment had been fought and lost and that it was an ideal that was being resigned by politicians and economists. This tough talk did not receive much support. Dave's friends felt there would always be businesses which would expand as far as the available workforce allowed. I'm forced to admit that theirs sounded the sensible conclusion. I was at a loss to tell them why, but I felt it was improbable. Dave agreed with me and later he spoke to me privately about what he considered his future employment prospects to be.

'I can't really see myself ever getting a proper job if I stay here. You yourself have only done what you've done by leaving the area where you came from [Turf Lodge]. Do you honestly think that if you stayed in West Belfast you'd be writing books or whatever? I'm unemployed because of where I was born. Middle-class fellas in this town don't have the handicaps that I have when I'm looking for work. I'm on the dole because I'm from Rathcoole. If I stay here, I'll be on the dole for the rest of my life. There's nothing I can do about where I was born but there is something I can do about where I live. I can leave. And I'm getting to the stage where I'm gonna have to go across the water [to England] pretty soon or else I'll be stuck here for ever. And if I stay here I'm dead – I'm worse than dead.'

I can't claim that I was comfortable spending time in Rathcoole. Much of the time I wandered the enormous estate prey to a range of portable emotions. It was hard for me to ignore that despite my neutral English accent, I was still a Catholic and one originating in 'Republican' West Belfast and as such, not really a visitor traditionally welcomed in areas like Rathcoole. The primacy of my origins might seem shaky now but as I walked past walls daubed with various crudely painted exhortations to dismember, obliterate or generally molest all Catholics, I felt outrageously, demonstrably Papist, as if I had the Hail Mary indelibly printed on my forehead. Did these guys have some kind of Taig-detecting radar? Was it gaps between your front teeth that meant you were a Catholic or was it the reverse? I ran my tongue over my most agnostic gums and worried.

Of course, nobody really gave the vaguest shit about my religion. Those I told seemed embarrassed that I had mentioned it or were merely uninterested. There *are* people who care. People who care passionately enough to do you harm, but they are a minority. Curious, isn't it? For a country that is ostensibly traumatized by sectarian violence, there seems to be a disconcertingly ecumenical majority in both communities.

Perhaps, the only advantage my ex-religion gave me was an opportunity to look more or less objectively at what had happened to working-class Protestantism in Belfast. West Belfast was always a cloudier aspect for me. There were too many remembered beauties in that place, too much child's view. In places like Rathcoole, I was as awash with unfamiliarity as I had been in darkest Hackney.

A great and foolish fantasy has been promulgated about the Protestant poor of Belfast for most of the twentieth century. A myth persists that the depressed Protestant areas of the city aren't as poor as similar Catholic enclaves – a surprisingly tenacious misapprehension.

A curious phenomenon operates in the class politics of Belfast and Northern Ireland. Much of the orthodox Protestant proletariat is so keen on protecting its faith and mores from Catholic incursions that they support a Loyalist status quo that is materially to their disadvantage. Belfast's middle classes do more than all right thank you. Belfast professionals have one of the highest rates of disposable income in the United Kingdom, due to the relatively low cost of property in the province. House prices here would make Home Counties folk weep. You can buy a four-bedroomed detached house in Belfast's leafiest desirable areas for around £40,000. You could swap the merest Stoke Newington rabbit hutch for a six-bedroomed Georgian listed building here. There are suburbs of Belfast where the Volvos, Mercedes and BMWs grow like grass.

This prosperity remains mostly the preserve of the Protestant middle class. Somehow, many working-class Protestants find more in common with their well-off brethren than with Catholic communities who suffer similar types of economic deprivation to themselves. This proportional wealth is culturally supported by a series of Protestant proletarian myths which concentrate on its denial to the Catholic minority. I met severely impoverished Protestant families who had to claim that their economic situation wasn't all that bad. Certainly not as bad as somewhere like Catholic West Belfast. It was as if the admission that a large number of the Protestant community is as effectively dispossessed as the Catholic minority was a dangerous, explosive notion hazardous to the idea that Unionist beliefs were beneficial to the Loyalist working class.

Rathcoole, Finaghy, Sandy Row, Ballybeen, Woodvale, Ballymacarret, Seymour Hill, The Village, Skegoniell, Annadale Flats and the Shankill. They're all Protestant areas and none are vignettes of success or plenty. Sixty-year-old Ronnie scrapes the graffiti from his front door every fortnight. It ranges from 'THE HOODS OF THIS ESTATE LIVE HERE' to 'JESUS SAVES' and 'THERE'S NO FIRE EXIT IN HELL'. He used to paint over it a couple of years ago but he can no longer afford the paint. Jack and Julie both live in Riverside. Julie is pregnant, neither works and both have brought previous debts with them from when they lived apart. Their expendable weekly income when I met them was £26 between them. Brian was a fourteen-year-old boy who showed me round Annadale flats. He and his three brothers were looked after by their twenty-four-year-old sister. Brian's attendance record at school was just over one day a week. He worked in the markets two days a week and was planning to leave school as soon as possible. His father had disappeared a decade before and his mother had been dead two years. Several social workers seemed to be writing memoirs about Brian. Brian could barely read, had never been in a restaurant or a cinema. He and his friends stole cars at night and drove them very fast around the Embankment. Considering Brian's other entertainment options, joy-riding, deadly and futile though it is, suddenly didn't seem an inexplicable pastime.

The poorest Protestant slices of the city are every bit as deprived or depressed as the more celebrated Catholic examples. Social workers and other professional poverty acolytes who deal with Loyalist areas of the city claim that the regions in which they work have social problems as severe as West Belfast or the New Lodge. I spoke to one social worker who operated in an overwhelmingly Protestant district. She was quick to anger over what she considered the relative lack of sympathy and understanding for the plight of people in her area. Too often, she believed, when people thought of a poor Irishman, they thought of a poor Catholic Irishman.

Protestant poverty undermines the foundations upon which Loyalist aspirations are based. Deprived Protestants are the most betrayed of all Ireland's communities. Their future is eternally mortgaged by the irresponsibility and insincerity of their demagogic representatives, official and unofficial. Though it could be argued that their areas are less directly traumatized by the twenty years of violence – there is less physical damage than in West Belfast, less rubble and wasteland – they are hurt by violence none the less. Economic and social damage has been done to the Protestant poor. They, too, have suffered from the paucity of capital investment that has bedevilled the country since the outbreak of the present conflict. They, too, have suffered fatalities and injury. They, too, have suffered the terrible moral degradation of living in a city where casual murder is routinely carried out in their name.

Rathcoole is a classic example of the 'greenfield estate', the large, rapidly planned and rapidly built housing area planted outside a city or town. It is a massive satellite dormitory whose conception belongs to an earlier generation. Its housing is a jumble (not blend) of high-rise blocks of flats, medium-rise maisonettes and more traditional self-contained two-storey homes. Shopping facilities are poor at best and transport to and from the city itself is completely inadequate. Community centres are relatively numerous and several local schools are conveniently situated, but healthcare facilities are less than moderate. Stalking the streets and greens of Rathcoole, you feel shut away from the city, you feel marginalized and remote.

The character of urban poverty has changed enormously in the last fifty years. The poorest of us are now slotted into areas which are hermetically sealed lest their contagion infect the more prosperous parts of the city. When George Orwell wrote about poverty in the thirties, deprived areas had their own economic microsystems in which small amounts of floating capital circulated and filtered out of the slums quite slowly. In the new (post-war) economic ghettos, it is much more difficult for the poor to maintain such microsystems. The institution of the modern Welfare State and the large-scale distribution of new benefits made circulation of relatively local capital impossible. Large amounts of capital income (which is, nevertheless, inadequate on the individual's scale) is injected into deprived areas by the Department of Social Security. The community is intermittently flooded with amounts of cash flimsy enough to be spent almost immediately. This capital is quickly creamed off by the true beneficiaries of the Welfare State – those who make it their business to cater for and systematically fleece the deprived. Hostels, b&b hotels like the one in which Alan Grant was living, local businesses and shops who are able to sell their goods at prices sometimes up to 30 per cent higher than in other areas of the same city, confident that their clientele's lack of effective transport means that these prices cannot be undercut by other businesses further away.

Rathcoole is an isolating factor in itself. It is being stifled and shackled by its site. It doesn't feel urban. It feels like Craigavon or Lurgan. The people who live in Rathcoole play a game called Hope. They have to concentrate hard to play. In Rathcoole, as in much of Protestant East Belfast, you must look beyond the fading red, white and blue painted on the kerbstones or the tattered flags and bullish murals. These seem emblems of a people with enough confidence and bellicosity to give away. This is not the case. Behind the banners and pulpy remonstrations, there is a lack of confidence. There is a glitch in the self-esteem of areas like Rathcoole.

Mick Wilson, his ears chafed by the hiked collar of his leather jacket, sat on a fence in Dunloy Gardens and told me that Rathcoole had only been a wasted opportunity in the past but that this could not continue indefinitely. One day, the potential of the people who lived there would be realized and employed to their benefit. According to Mick, Rathcoole was protected by its size – it was simply too big to ignore. It would be like ignoring a town.

The longer Mick talked, the less assured he seemed. I didn't make any of the kind of sceptical and unwelcome comments which I had made with Dave's friends. I kept my own counsel. Mick's vision of improvement for Rathcoole certainly wasn't impossible. Nothing was truly impossible for or in Rathcoole. It was just much more difficult than it might have been.

I spent a couple of weeks with Mick and his family. Mick was a thirty-three-year-old ex-UDR man. He had left the UDR (a regiment of the British Army locally recruited and stationed solely in Ulster) about six years ago. He had worked as a security guard for a couple of years afterwards, during which time he had met his wife, Justine. Justine was five years older than Mick and already had two children from a previous marriage. A year after they wed, Mick lost his job. Two weeks later, Justine gave birth to Sarah, her only daughter.

Mick was on the dole now but he let that interfere with his life as little as possible. Mick liked going out but he didn't like going out with his wife. One of the most eloquent testaments to a man's character is the way he treats his wife. Mick was scrupulous and attentive when at home with Justine but such behaviour seemed to belong solely to the family home. Outside, Mick preferred the company of men and what he saw as exclusively male pursuits. He often mentioned his distaste for his wife's company to me but claimed that he still loved her. I asked him why he had married Justine. He told me that he had felt isolated and depressed after leaving the UDR and having to give up the flat he then occupied. He told me that getting married made him feel like a man again. This anomaly tallied with some of the marriages I had encountered among other people I met over those months. There seemed, in circumstances of poverty, a great desire for the emotional prosperity of marriage.

Mick took me gambling with him several times. We divided our time between betting shops and the dog races at Dunmore Stadium near Skegoniell. I had never gambled before. Mick betted convulsively – a series of moderate bets interspersed with risks he simply could not afford. It surprised me to see him gamble so passionately. He was not a stupid or even imprudent man and yet he seemed to abandon all of his normally sceptical outlook when he gambled.

I felt that this was another reaction to the kind of necessary fatalism that had so daunted me in Hackney. There, I had noticed the outrageous plans, the dreams of prosperity. Gambling is just another form of the fantasy of unlikely prosperity. For someone with little income, games of chance can seem like gaudy beacons of sadly impossible hopes. Indeed, with so little opportunity for anything like monetary investment and with the risible sums of money habitually available to the poor, gambling can seem a fairly imaginative form of venture capitalism. And the dream of the lucky break accumulates likelihood even in the face of repeated loss. The dividends are so tempting. (It is fallacious to imagine that the poor can't imagine what it's like to be wealthy. This is easy to imagine. Everyone in Hackney, Ballymurphy and Rathcoole has very detailed plans for it.)

Gambling when you're poor is suicidal. Gambling almost never pays off. Its attraction is the foggy lure of the big win. But big wins depend on big stakes. Big stakes are only really possible for those with a level of income where big wins don't make *that* much difference. Big wins are unlikely for those who can only afford to place small bets. The logic is cruel but undeniable.

Losing is also a very different experience for those on low income. Losing is not only a financial blow more catastrophic than you can bear, it's also a humiliation. Abruptly, your dream of big dividends seems so shoddy and childish. The spending round that you might have planned for yourself, your wife and children is shaming. You watch the casual gamblers who accept their wins or losses with equal insouciance. That seems more like the real man's world, the world from which you are excluded. For you, gambling is true hazard. You hope too much. You need to win too badly.

The first night I spent at Dunmore with Mick was an astonishing experience. If the poorest men had not already announced themselves by their shabbiness, they would still have been easy to spot by the extent of their dejection when they lost. The five-pound bet seemed to be their *modus operandi*. It occurred to me that five pounds was a sum their families might have been glad of. Most men made at least two or three such bets and the waste was disgraceful. To their credit, they were fully aware of that and the sums they lost haunted them with implacable accusations of improvidence and dissipation. One of Mick's friends, a middle-aged catering worker with four teenage children, gambled away nearly a hundred pounds. He told me that it was the flesh and bones of a fortnight's take-home pay. His shame was visceral. When the meet was over, this man blinked rapidly as if the lights had been trained on him suddenly. He looked pinned down and accused. He looked tortured. I tried to lend him some cash but he refused and left. Mick told me he never won.

Though it was difficult to spend much time with Justine when Mick wasn't there, we did manage to have a couple of lengthy conversations. Justine was admirably clement about Mick's foibles. She had worked out that Mick's frivolous inroads into their joint income cost them more than half their combined benefit. Her tolerance of this seemed, for some reason

I can't quite understand, to show more benevolence than weakness.

'Mick's sometimes foolish with money and he likes to have his nights out and all that but you've seen him with the kids. He's a good father and he's even a good father to the two that aren't his – it's not every fella from round here who'd be like that. He misses his time in the UDR. He still tries to see as many of his old friends that were in the force with him. When he's with them, he likes to be able to spend as much money as they do. The difference is that they're earning a good wage and half of them are still single. But I understand why he does it. He doesn't want them to take pity on him because he's on the dole. And in a way, he's just right.'

Justine managed the home and children on the half of their income that remained after Mick's largesse. The money at her disposal was so limited that her life was a consistent series of crises – incidental and impossible emergencies that she could barely afford, if at all. Dentists, doctors and opticians plagued her and her children. She had nightmares about shoes. The shoe problem *was* extraordinary. Her children's feet grew like mutant hothouse plants. Shoes collapse abruptly, and a vicious circle operates whereby cheap shoes fall apart fastest. Unexpectedly large bills arrived by the sack and her kitchen electricals waited for her to spend her fortnight's allowance before exploding.

'It's as if, the less money you have, the more emergencies you have,' explained Justine. 'I used to sit and cry when things got on top of me but now I actually laugh. It's funny sometimes when things just go on getting worse when you already think that they're as bad as they can ever be. There are things I don't even tell Mick now. I used to go on at him if there was a bill to pay or we were getting behind with the rent or something but now I don't bother. It didn't get me anywhere when I did try to get at him. It's not worth the hassle now. He can't bear thinking about money except when he's spending it. I think sometimes he convinces himself that he's not poor when he's spending money. And that's harmless enough most of the time. Why spoil it for him?'

Rathcoole is the wintry gut of Belfast. It can seem surreal with its size and strange grandeur. It is a De Chirico dream, cold and imperfect. Rathcoole exists – it is a physical place with houses, bricks, mortar and cement – but Rathcoole feels like an idea and a bad one at that. The estate is someone's brainchild, some fatuous town planner's favourite baby. Somebody said, 'Let's build Rathcoole' and, lo, Rathcoole indeed was built. Arbitrary is not the word.

I said earlier that the poorest communites are now gathered up into groups and deposited into estates. This gives them no chance to grow or evolve. It is my impression that cities grow most comfortably over generations, that left to themselves they will spread themselves slowly like ink on paper. People come, jobs come; jobs come, people come. A (shaky perhaps) rule of supply and demand operates and an enlightened municipal authority can help a city grow as much as it needs. Post-war estates destroy any possibility of progress or change within the poorest communities. These places are not adaptable. Rathcoole, particularly, is murdered by its size. Rathcoole cannot expand or grow. There is nowhere for Rathcoole to grow. Recession or boom, Rathcoole must stay constant and unchanging. No economic swings in its surrounding region can produce much expansion or growth for a Rathcoole. It's a very finalized place. Arbitrary is certainly not the word.

SIX

At some point one has to ask how much Belfast's political violence contributes to its poverty. Or, how much does Belfast's poverty contribute to its political violence?

Violence of the barbarity and scale that has so marked Belfast in the last twenty years cannot fail to handicap a city's prosperity. Despite the sultry blandishments of the Industrial Development Board and its offers of massive subsidies for businesses investing in the province, Belfast chronically lacks capital investment. The spiralling cost of insurance in a city waiting for bomb attacks is prohibitive. Occasionally, the IRA decides that a particular business or type of business is an economic arm of the 'British War Machine' and starts blowing the crap out of it regularly. That can be costly in both money and jobs – *local* jobs.

Also, the British government's main expenditure in Northern Ireland is devoted to the massive security effort in the province. The RUC, the UDR and those regiments of the British Army stationed here are expensive. Their presence and the restrictions this brings inhibit commercial enterprise. Every time the police have to shut down the city centre because of bomb scares, real or imaginary, countless thousands of pounds' worth of trade and business are lost. The extra costs imposed on local businesses by the region's multiple peculiarities lead to an increase in their products' prices which greatly reduces export potential so that too many businesses have to concentrate their trading efforts on Northern Ireland itself – a market much too small to support business strength or expansion.

The ways in which Belfast's deprivation perpetuates the city's violence are multiple and complex. Certainly, the ostensible catalyst for the present violence was the civil rights marches of the late sixties. These movements directly called for Catholic employment rights among other basic civil liberties. After the barbarous and violent reaction of the Protestant majority to these modest demands, the struggle for civil rights was quickly hijacked by a paramilitary campaign on a much wider scale and seeking vastly different resolutions. The speed with which demands for civil liberties was commandeered into nationalistic violence is easily explained by the long and depressing history of Ulster's literal dispossession of its Catholic minority. The poverty and great grievance of that community had mounted up through generations of deprivation and marginalization. When it blew, it really blew.

And yet despite all this, it is Belfast's poorest who suffer the worst effects of the city's violence, economically and physically. The death toll among the Belfast bourgeoisie in no way matches that sustained by the city's working class. And then there's the inordinate prosperity that Belfast's highest earners still enjoy. The privileges of Belfast's suburbia seem to protect them from most of the cost and most of the dying.

Much, if not all, of the city's violence emanates from its poorest areas. Protestant paramilitaries engage themselves in a war largely against the Catholic proletariat. Catholic paramilitaries conduct their violence against the security forces – against mainly working-class men or women economically conscript in those hazardous occupations. (Catholic paramilitaries also do a fair bit of harm to other Catholics). And yet, Belfast's violence fatally redounds against both working-class communities – it is they who suffer, cumulatively and separately.

I think that this self-destructive violence continues to be endured by the peaceful majorities in both communities because these deracinated peoples have so little left to lose. What more can someone lose when they've already lost their chance? In areas already murdered and redundant with poverty, the most atavistic savagery can make little real difference.

In the morbid and necrophiliac traditions of Ireland, dispossession and violence have never been far removed. Since the institution of the state of the Irish Republic, the moral history of Ireland's great violence has been cosmetically altered. A kind of sanctity now attaches to figures whose methods and ideals were barbaric and irresponsible. When a state is created through violence, the historians are always uneasy. Statehood confers sudden respectability and stature upon dissidents, seditionaries and terrorists. It is important that we do not blind ourselves to how self-destructive much of Ireland's historical violence has been. Or to how much more the poor have suffered compared with other sections of Irish society.

Perhaps the most startling way that Belfast's violence has materially affected the lives of its least prosperous citizens is in the area of housing. Surprisingly, in the last ten years, Belfast's public housing provision has been such that Belfast now has some of the finest council housing of any of the regions in which Donovan and I spent our time. Its most recent advances are generally a stunning success. The housing that envelops the Shankill and Lower Falls area, the very birthplace of violence two decades ago, has been mostly rebuilt in the past ten years. My father lives in one of these new houses in Sevastopol Street, with his second wife and her teenage daughter. They have two bathrooms and excellent central heating from a smokeless fuel fire in the main room. Their kitchen is enviably large and spacious. The home is well insulated and has its own small front and back gardens. It is spacious, bright with large windows and well constructed.

Ballymurphy, Springhill, Divis, The Markets, Ballymacarret, Taughmonagh and parts of the New Lodge are among the areas most benefiting from housebuilding initiatives taken in Northern Ireland in the last decade. The new housing is overwhelmingly red-brick two-storey self-contained homes and of uniformly excellent quality. Belfast seems to have rejected the high-rise completely.

Although a number of factors explain the administrative efforts to improve housing in Belfast, one of the main reasons must have been sectarian violence. The present troubles began with Catholic families being chased from their homes by Protestant mobs who lived in the locale. It wasn't long before Protestants who lived in mainly Catholic areas were also compelled to leave. In the ensuing years of violence, intimidation, housing and relocation remained some of the dominant issues. There were several flashpoint areas in the city where Protestant and Catholic enclaves simmered in close proximity. In areas such as the Falls/Shankill middle ground, the Crumlin Road/Cliftonville interface or the isolatedly Catholic Short Strand, communities began to shift and warp haphazardly as individual families suffered intimidation or outright violence from their alternatively faithed neighbours. Most of the pogroms faded away after the first few years of mayhem but, by that time, the map of Belfast's communities had already warped and buckled.

It came to be seen that, apart from any general social improvement, provision of sensitively planned housing could relieve a great many of the extra pressures and worst social effects of sectarian violence. I don't think anyone thought that an effective public housebuilding programme was going to end the 'troubles' but many felt that it would do much to defuse certain potentially or actually explosive situations.

Thus, Belfast's culture of political violence helped to cause one of the most laudable public housing schemes in Great Britain. This is not to say that *all* the public housing in Belfast is a masterpiece. There are still some remnants of a less sensitive era of public planning. Donovan's photographs of Rathcoole and the box homes of Springhill are more eloquent than any catalogue of outrage from me. I'm glad to say that even in the few months since he photographed Springhill, most of those remaining oblong obscenities have been demolished. A similar fate awaits the great shame of Belfast, Divis Flats.

The speed and scope of the city's great housing changes would have been impossible without the Housing Executive. Housing in Northern Ireland is not in the remit of local authorities: a central, province-wide Housing Executive deals with all Northern Ireland's public housing. The Executive was created in 1971 and the responsibility for housing passed to it from sixty-five local authorities. Centralization is a contemporary bugbear in British political life but in the isolated example of Northern Ireland's housing conditions it has proved itself effective.

The advantages of such centralization were multiple. An organization of the Housing Executive's size was a more effective claimant upon central government's attention and resources. Administrative costs were reduced in that a single authority obviously suffers less duplication of resources than a series of smaller autonomous agencies. Resources could be used more effectively and budgets planned and expended with greater consistency. Consistency would also be the main improvement in single unified rent and allocation policies. Any success that the Executive might claim for itself stems largely from the consistency and breadth of vision that it was able to bring to bear on Belfast's housing nightmare.

The difficulties that faced the new Executive in the seventies were enormous. The extent of the neglect and dereliction of Belfast's poorest housing was atonishing. Conditions in many parts of the city were desperate – cramped, crumbling houses with inadequate sanitation or heating. Estates had been planted squat all over the city since the fifties and sixties. The urban developments of those periods were already showing their age and unsuitability, and the city also had its share of high-rise or medium-rise low-quality housing which, in the prevailing atmosphere of political violence, became even more untenable.

Indeed, Ivan Maginnis of the Executive's Information Centre was uncomfortable with my assertion that public housing in

Belfast was among the best in Britain. He was more prone to claiming that it was among the worst. There is something in that: the Executive's most recent initiatives have been, of necessity, gradual and in the areas which have yet to be tackled by the rebuilding programme conditions *are* largely disgraceful and abject. Despite Maginnis's reticence however, I still maintain that the most recent efforts in housing in the city are effective and consistent to a degree unheard of in much of London or Glasgow.

This great improvement dates from 1981 when the province's housing under the aegis of Jim Prior became a prime social priority for the Conservative government. A statistic that has been much exercised in the last few years is that in the eighties expenditure on housing per head of population in Northern Ireland was four times greater than elsewhere in Britain. If such is the case, that discrepancy in resources must also go a long way towards explaining the Executive's most recent successes.

The eighties saw a widespread rejection of the public housing precepts of the sixties and seventies. The love of dormitory estates with high-rise blocks and the stress on population density per square mile evaporated. A return to more traditional housing was deemed desirable. Two-storey, self-contained housing became the main focus of the Housing Executive's planning energies. In some cases, this led and leads to the destruction of high-rise or medium-rise estates which are rebuilt with the kind of two-storey houses that had existed before the lofty concrete towers were built. I believe that in Divis the street plans of the old area are even being used to plan the replacement and reconstruction of that blighted estate.

Low-rise housing is ultimately preferable to high-rise. (Notice that the middle classes never rushed to build their homes skyward.) The new emphasis on low-rise housing gives control of the area's environment back to the residents. The effect of having your own front door open on to the street or your own bit of garden is incalculable but benign. Taughmonagh is an estate of new (ten-year-old) houses that lies between Kingsway and the Upper Malone Road to the south of the city. The entire estate was rebuilt. The previous accommodation had been aluminium bungalows built after the Blitz. (Belfast suffered extensively from German bombing during the Second World War.) Conditions on the old estate had been embarrassingly bad and Taughmonagh was an obvious priority for reconstruction.

Within ten years the area was transformed: those living in the old tin bungalows were rehoused in the competently built new houses. The Housing Executive's policy is to resettle communities in their original area after rebuilding and the replacement of housing stock is phased to permit this and reduce community disruption. I hardly need to mention that this is better than shifting a whole community to somewhere new: communities able to reoccupy their own rebuilt areas are stabilized communities.

The residents of Taughmonagh form a community which has been allowed to remain stable as its housing was replaced. The estate has reaped incalculable benefit from this. A social worker who spends much of his working life there tells me that since the new estate was built an obvious reduction in the area's social problems has resulted. The Taughmonagh people to whom I spoke could still hardly believe their luck. They were grateful to see the back of the old tin huts. Ivan Maginnis had told me that the final and only substantial comment on the efficacy of the Housing Executive must come from its clients.

The improvements in other areas of the city have not been perhaps as spectacular as in Taughmonagh (which is relatively small), though the reconstruction of the Markets areas has also been truly remarkable. Other areas are tackled more gradually in phased bursts of demolition and construction, gradually but competently throughout the city.

Such large-scale, far-reaching improvements have only been possible because of the Housing Executive's unofficial long-term planning. The Executive receives its income annually like other public housing bodies in Britain. However, it draws up three-year plans and budgets. It can plan on an expected income of, say, £300 million for three years. If the Executive were to receive only 95 million in one of those three years, plans could be readjusted without having to react drastically to sudden budget cuts, which lends a breadth of vision and planning on a large scale that would be impossible with more short-term budgeting procedures.

The situation in much of London contrasts markedly with the opportunities available in Belfast. For example, local authority housing in Islington is divided into twenty-four autonomous local offices, which have their own estate managers and letting officers etc., though some of them share premises and repair teams. Islington's budgets are strictly annual and their planning is almost entirely yearly as well. There are a number of 'rolling programmes' for certain small-scale initiatives but no major manoeuvres can be planned long term. Central government cuts and new wrinkles like the poll tax were further tightening the limitations on Islington's exercise of foresight. I asked Islington whether they would have preferred the opportunity for greater longer-range planning. They replied that they lay awake at nights dreaming of such things.

Tower Hamlets is in a similar position, though there are only seven local neighbourhood offices there, governed by the political representatives elected in each ward. Once again, committees are autonomous and have some budgeting freedom. The folk at Tower Hamlets seemed much keener to stress the advantages of their system, emphasizing the greater local accountability that results from such a devolved system of administration and allocation. With local offices, they felt that there was much greater opportunity for those people who were, after all, the clients of public housing to make known their demands and their criticisms.

However, the Housing Executive, centralized and massive though it is, caters for a fair degree of local accountability. The Executive has numerous estate-based sub-offices that open several days a week. Administration descends in tiers from central authority, regional and local authority. There are even mobile offices for those living in Northern Ireland's sparsely populated countryside. Thus local accountability can be achieved while retaining a large enough organization to put it into widespread effect. Priorities may also be judged with greater justice and foresight.

Like Islington, Tower Hamlets has a number of 'rolling programmes'. Tower Hamlets say that these programmes are large scale, unlike those of Islington, but that the programmes are prey to the inconsistency of central government funding. While central government continually cajoles local authorities to plan ahead, Tower Hamlets sees no reward for its own attempts at planning foresight. Central government might favour a particular kind of housing scheme one year and completely reject it the next. Government fads change quite abruptly. Thus local authorities have to bias their capital programme bids to central government towards whatever type of scheme is currently in favour. (When I spoke to Tower Hamlets, schemes to improve security on estates were the current golden boy.)

Ivan Maginnis felt that the Housing Executive avoids such difficulties because it does not suffer from the kind of political tensions between local and central government which are prevalent in London. In London, boroughs controlled by a political party different from the party in government might find a reluctant central government ear for their claims and proposals. In Northern Ireland, such difficulties are very unlikely.

In England as in Scotland and Wales, the situation is too often that in housing, political decisions are made first and housing decisions second. In Northern Ireland, politicians are largely uninvolved in housing policy decision making. Therefore the bias of Housing Executive bids and proposals is not towards what they feel the politicians might like but is, in fact, a bias towards whatever actual housing need they feel worthy of priority.

So, if you were to identify the ingredients for an adequate public housing system, two of the most essential components would be the possibility of long-term budgeting and planning and the avoidance of political tinkering. Through a variety of extreme local pressures and unique social problems, Northern Ireland has managed to achieve an approximation of both.

Belfast's violence involves its citizens in dreadful moral degradation. In various ways, the city's violence is executed in the name of its citizens. However fictional or flimsy this mandate may be, the degradation remains. Obviously, this degradation caused by violence must be greatest for those citizens most exposed to the city's violence. In Belfast, the most exposed are the poorest. Thus the mental and moral harm caused by the violent convulsions of Northern Ireland is greater for the area's deprived.

Simply: the violence makes the poor poorer. It makes the city more hopeless, easier to leave. The gross sectarian division eradicates the possibility of united struggle for the dispossessed in Belfast. The poor divide their vote into two – their traditional powerlessness is doubled. It is then trebled or quadrupled by Northern Ireland's province status. In Northern Ireland, the country's poor (like everyone else here) cannot actually vote for anyone that might conceivably govern them. It's hard to imagine a time when a local party will wield administrative power. SDLP, DUP, OUP, Alliance, Sinn Fein and Workers' Party – they claim great differences, these parties, but they resemble each other in their impotence. In that, they're much of a muchness. This means that Northern Ireland's electorate are like ignored children, rewarded every few generations with the balance of power in a hung parliament. What strange version of democracy is this?

The violence makes Belfast two cities – a Protestant city and a Catholic city. Two impoverished cities needing two separate solutions. All measures taken to alleviate deprivation must be duplicated and minutely balanced – one for Catholics and one for Protestants. A Catholic community will not use a resource placed in a Protestant community and vice versa. A Protestant community will complain bitterly if it feels that any new development is of greatest advantage to Catholics and vice versa. And all the time both communities exercise their stalemate franchise and surrender themselves to political parties who thrive on the weary hatreds of a half-remembered history.

Often now, I get unhappy when I think about Belfast's future or futures. Of all Britain's cities, I suppose the likelihoods and possibilities are more multiple and complex for Belfast. But in strictly economic terms, the future seems to be bleak at best and possibly catastrophic. We live in a dying boom town with dead industries where, it might be argued, the disproportionate size of public sector activity fatally inhibits the growth of the private sector. Whatever one's views on the legality or desirability of British involvement in Northern Ireland (and these views split less cleanly down sectarian lines than is imagined), it is difficult to ignore the idea that British involvement (underpinning) in the province is simply postponing its future. It is also difficult to know how long it can last or what new social and economic mutations might emerge. In the meantime, more crucially than anywhere else in Britain, Belfast's future is mortgaged.

SEVEN

Poverty has changed. It has grown worse. In a generation of tax cuts for the well off and rising living standards for the majority, the contrast of poverty with affluence has grown sharper. The agencies and structures which determine the lives of the poor have been restricted, capped and cut back steadily for ten years or more. Industrial decline or irresponsible monetarism has fatally eroded much of the working class's traditional employment base. Whole manufacturing towns have been stifled and many communities have ruptured in the resulting economic depressions.

The Department of Social Security is less adequate than ever. Manning has been drastically cut while demand for the Department's services has exploded. Budgetary tinkering, both in benefit allowance and in administration, further handicap the work that the DSS might do – delay and incompetence are inescapable. Now, if you're claiming benefit in London you often have to speak to an official in Belfast or Glasgow on a special DSS telephone line in your local DSS office. This seems lunatic to me, the Circumlocution Office at its worst.

This kind of deterioration or decay in the services used by the deprived leads to a further degradation of their ability to manage their affairs effectively. When your income depends on an agency which is suffering cutbacks in administrative efficiency and budget, your income is shaky. Local government cuts lead to sharp declines in the management of public housing. Conditions can slide with awesome speed and repairs become something of a joke when council labour budgets cannot be exceeded. There is now an optimum season for your walls to crack or your plumbing to break down, when you're not too badly off. If your home falls down round your ears after the local authority has exceeded its labour budget, then you're fucked.

Benefit delays (which can be lengthy and reasonless) can cause – almost always cause – dire hardship. A couple of weeks or more without a Giro can lead to debt, disconnection or catastrophe. Poverty has become even more completely a matter of barely surviving from one crisis to another. The benefit rule changes that have been introduced in the last five years have made such crisis management much more difficult: planning or prudence is impossible when income has been so drastically reduced. The oppressive circle of reduced circumstances in which the poor live is being tightened further by a government unwilling to assume responsibility for the consequences of its economic heavy hand.

The penalties faced by the deprived, if they fail to see through their multiple and regular crises, fall into three groups: DEP – Disconnection, Eviction and Prosecution. Disconnection of electricity is perhaps the most widespread although the boards are quick to publicize that they do not disconnect elderly people or families during the winter. What they do not advertise is that they disconnect elderly people and families during the warmer months and are happy to extend the period of disconnection into the following winter. They *never* reconnect out of charitable concern.

Eviction is much less common, certainly in Northern Ireland. In London, it is rather more routine, particularly for those who are squatting in council property. Eviction is an indescribable, appalling experience. It is also an extraordinary measure for any local authority to take since they most always have a legal obligation to house the evicted tenants. This is not to say that council tenants should be free not to pay their rents if they don't feel like it but massive rent arrears are usually accumulated through a variety of other severe financial pressures. Arrears are rarely due to insouciance or an attempt to defraud and a little sympathy and understanding can bring constructive rewards without having to resort to the brute foolishness of eviction.

Prosecution for debt, social-security fraud or other criminal offences is the staple diet of the poor's dealings with the law. The first is easily the most common. Courts enforce repayment of arrears by instructing the DSS to deduct certain sums from the debtor's benefit payments. Courts rarely neglect to add a hefty fine to add to his or her difficulties. An interesting legal loophole exists in Scotland whereby poor people in debt can declare themselves bankrupt; after a set number of years, three or five, their debts are written off. This benevolent discrepancy for the Scottish poor is, by all accounts, doomed. Apparently, the Government is keen to close this loophole lest any of its lessons filter down to the poorest debtors in the rest of Great Britain.

Hally, with whom this book opened, was about to shoulder the weight of legal opprobrium on two fronts: he was to be prosecuted over his rent arrears and was also due to appear on a shop-lifting charge. The compulsory-care order which robbed him of his children had also been legally endorsed. The law had hammered him from all sides. He had been and would be robbed of much of what he considered important: his children, his home and his liberty.

On top of their practical trials and obstacles, the dispossessed are subject to the moral prodding of the rest of society. Everybody seems to have an opinion and moral stance on poverty, its exponents and extent. The better-off sections of society feel it their right to make all kinds of comments and moral recommendations about how the poor should lead or improve their lives. 'Why don't they get a job?' 'Why don't they stop having so many children?' 'Why don't they take a course of adult education?' 'Why don't they make adequate provision for their children?' 'Why do they smoke or drink or bet (or breathe)?' 'Why don't they improve themselves?'

For many of the people I met in the past year these suggestions would be either absurd or unwelcome. You might as well advise them to win a gold medal in the Olympic one hundred metres. If this self-help stuff was easy or even possible, don't you think they'd do it? Self-help has become a vicious and patronizing fiction which is deployed to excuse society's neglect of its lowest earners.

Such moral cowardice stems from a refusal to comprehend poverty as a moral or political issue as well as a social one. Poverty is ultimately political. Indeed, contemporary poverty owes its scale and intensity to one particular brand of political orthodoxy: 'Thatcherism' is a dogma which has produced a cosmetic and flimsy economic boom. One of the costs of this temporary chimera has been the further impoverishment of the poorest quarter of the population. This price has been set by central government without equivocation of any kind.

Government techniques for dealing with the poor also betray an inability to accept responsibility for their conditions. The arms of the state that deal with poverty have become unconscionably more punitive in the past ten years. Social services are increasingly finding their role moulded and reduced by financial cutbacks: they are becoming the moral snatch-squads for the rest of society. The current levels of state benefit are unspeakably inadequate. Gerneral policy in housing seems to be dictated by a heady blend of whim and ignorance. The law is being increasingly employed as a poor-bashing mallet and the police are now forced into a role of circumvention and control which they cannot properly fulfil.

(Certainly, in Hackney I noticed that the police were forced into some unusual postures. Henry Richards and his friends, young black males, were subjected to fairly considerable harassment, a depressing example of which I witnessed myself. But you don't have to be black to get grief. In Kingsmead, compulsory care orders, evictions and suchlike were often accompanied by an excessive police contingent and young white males suffered an only slightly less constant scrutiny from the police.)

This kind of police and legal hassle of the deprived isn't due to the police being wicked or the law evil. Such state chivvying of a community parallels much of the security activity prevalent in Northern Ireland. The police, when confronted by a problem that they cannot solve – a political problem – can only resort to persistent harassment of a particular public. Hackney's deprivation is as much a political problem as Belfast's violence. But police and law are increasingly seen as the broom that will sweep the political dust of dispossession under the carpet and middle-class complacency is a big enough rug to hide it well.

'*The poor will be with us always.*' In Britain, as elsewhere, there is a growing base of cultural support for the idea that there is, of economic necessity, a certain tolerable level of poverty in society. Recent economic strategies have raised the living standards of some sections of British society while causing ever greater hardship for that society's least prosperous communities. For those who have benefited, increases in poverty can be seen as merely unfortunate side-effects, unavoidable and incurable. We seem to trundle along quite happily with the notion of an inevitable poor.

It seems we are capable of accepting that a certain fraction or percentage of our society lives in poverty. It is hard to know exactly what kind of figure might be liveable with for the majority – a fifth, a quarter, perhaps even a third? At what stage would the situation become intolerable? The acceptance of a permanent and ineradicable poor is seen as laudably realistic – a rational rather than dystopian view. It's simply not good enough.

We all have to assume the moral responsibility for the poverty in our society. The moral responsibility *is* ours. In many ways, the *empirical* responsibility is ours. In any number of smudged, complicated ways, our prosperity is dependent on their dispossession. We take from them. We must let this conviction spoil our dinner.

I'm forced to wonder what chance there is that this tolerance of poverty by the prosperous might change. It would require an unprecedented moral, cultural and political shift for British society to reject the idea that poverty, if not necessary, is at least inevitable. The possibility of most of us ceasing to tolerate conditions which do not affect us and of which we are mostly ignorant is not great. We seem to have an immoderate capacity for finding bearable the suffering of others.

I have said before that this book is a failure or, at best, a book about failure. The more I've written, the greater this conviction has grown. Some parts of it were written much too fast, some too slowly. I lost the notes for one chapter on a Circle Line tube station. I didn't even stay in Glasgow for much more than a weekend, a dereliction of intent which I cannot excuse.

I never really discovered how to write this book. A year and more ago, it seemed a fairly simple undertaking. I already felt so much about poverty – I set out with chapterfuls of opinions and theories. None of them survived actual contact with the newest mutations of British poverty. I had spent much of my own life in poverty but the deprivation I encountered in the past year was very different.

The list of things I didn't write about is long and shaming. I didn't write about the many community groups which do such substantial work in deprived areas, I didn't write about pensions and the elderly, poverty among the disabled community. I didn't write about poverty's international context, about labour relations, workers' rights, the minimum wage or women's disadvantages in the labour market. I didn't write about employment training or enterprise schemes. I didn't write about how drastically the poor are affected by the degradation of the National Health Service. Even those things I did write about, I didn't write about in enough detail.

But perhaps my failure is as eloquent as any competence would have been. Perhaps this failure demonstrates how truly desperate the situation is for Britain's contemporary poor. I could not cope with nor adequately describe their conditions. I failed to record sufficiently the anguish of the people whom Donovan and I met. Their plight was more than I had bargained for.

Donovan's photographs are, at least, firmly rooted in the pragmatic actuality of what he saw. He took the risk of taking pictures that could not be pretty but, within that, he has created real beauty. His pictures demonstrate, better than anything I could have written, the contradictions in what we encountered. He captured both the appalling conditions and the real grandeur of people whose dignity and stature survived their predicament.

If anything, this book is simply a complaint. We'd like to complain, please. We have no answers and our understanding of the issues is perhaps rudimentary but we'd still like to complain.

We hope that we have not seemed to establish any kind of proprietorship over righteous indignation or moral certainty. We don't have exclusive moaning rights over poverty and its trials (the poor themselves have pretty watertight copyright there). It's tempting to fulminate about people's capacity to tolerate or dismiss poverty. But it's foolish. I can only believe that most of the unsympathetic attitudes towards poverty stem from ignorance. I believe that most people, whatever their politics, would feel angry and diminished in some way if they were to encounter for themselves the kind of dispossession which Donovan and I witnessed.

Sometimes, poverty seems to form a marshy foundation for a society's economic structures. Booms and recessions dilute or solidify that flimsy base, reducing or enlarging its extent. Whether tackled or ignored, poverty is bedevilled and abetted by legislative inconsistency, modish political doctrine and simple economic incompetence. One thing is certain: recently, the idea that the poor will be always with us has gained firm ground. Poverty is being rendered ever more tolerable. The notion of its permanence is making poverty's marshy foundations adamantine. The idea is hardening into a crust in all our minds.